Complex PTSD

Understanding PTSD's Effects on Brain, Body and Emotions - Healing from Childhood Trauma

Erika Alexander

Table of Contents

Introduction

P TSD usually starts soon after the traumatic event, but sometimes not until years later. People with PTSD often have frightening thoughts or dreams related to the event, feel emotionally numb and disconnected, or have angry outbursts, depression, and reviews of suicide. A person can experience PTSD symptoms after any traumatic situation.

This event might be something they've seen, such as in news reports, something they've heard about; something they've read about, or something that has happened to them. It's normal to feel frightened or stressed when you see or hear these news reports on the TV, radio, internet, etc. However, some people feel stressed or frightened for weeks or months after such the triggering event.

They may have bad dreams about the event and feel easily startled. These symptoms can interfere with everyday life. The person might be unable to go to places that remind him/her of the event, have problems falling asleep, sleep too much, feel detached from their family and friends, or get angry quickly.

These feelings and reactions are all part of PTSD. Many people who experience trauma have these symptoms first, but they get better in a few weeks or months. For others, the signs last much longer and get worse if they don't get help. It is essential to seek help if you are affected by these symptoms.

Trauma can be caused by a single event or exposure to an extreme stressor PTSD develops after the person has experienced or witnessed a life-threatening event that may have involved physical harm or the threat of physical harm to themselves or others around them and which often results in feelings of extreme fear, helplessness, or horror.

To be diagnosed with PTSD, symptoms must last longer than one month and cause significant distress or problems functioning in daily life. Along with the psychological symptoms above, there can be physical ones. Treatment is available for PTSD, and can be very effective in helping people who have been affected by traumatic events to recover from their psychiatric illness. It is essential to know that there are treatments that work.

The treatment approach for PTSD is based on the knowledge that symptoms can be treated, and people can recover. When a person with PTSD starts to feel better, they will need to learn how to cope better in the future in situations that remind them of their traumatic event. This condition may return, but it often gets better with each subsequent episode of care.

Several different methods can treat PTSD:

Medication: Medicines are not usually given for PTSD because the symptoms are stress responses and usually resolve on their own over time. However, medicines may help when people have very severe symptoms or depression simultaneously as PTSD.

Psychotherapy: One of the best-proven treatments is cognitive behavior therapy. It is a form of talking therapy where a trained therapist works with the person to:

Cognitive Behavioral Therapy (CBT): This involves exposing people to situations that remind them of their worst trauma and teaching them relaxation techniques. Compulsory disclosure, role play, and anxiety management are often used in combination with other therapies. CBT can help people who have PTSD in more complicated situations. People have successfully allowed by learning how to accept their fears and manage anxiety, such as relaxation techniques or breathing exercises.

Eye Movement Desensitization Reprocessing (EMDR): This is a form of psychotherapy that involves following eye movements as the therapist moves their fingers from left to right. These memories are then reactivated by stimuli in everyday life. EMDR helps people accept their traumatic experiences and improve mood, behavior, sleep, concentration, and functioning.

Group therapy: Some research has suggested that group CBT may be more effective for PTSD than individual CBT. This involves a group of eight or more people with similar problems meeting regularly to receive CBT.

Eye Movement Desensitization and Reprocessing (EMDR): Developed by Francine Shapiro, Ph.D., EMDR is a psychological treatment used with people who have experienced trauma. The technique combines eye movements or other forms of rhythmic, left-to-right stimulation with different forms of verbal input to re-duce the intensity of disturbing memories or distress associated with them in a manner that psychologists are still exploring. In addition to standard EMDR therapy, other approaches incorpo-rate additional elements, such as EMDR guided self-help and therapist-assisted self-administered treatments.

If you have symptoms for more than a month and they're having an impact on your life – especially if you feel like hurting yourself or others – it's essential to get help right away. The following in-formation is not meant to label anyone or to take away your right to make an informed decision about your treatment. It provides an explanation of some of the factors that have led the committee to conclude that this disorder should be included in the next edi-tion of the diagnostic manual.

On 15 December 2004, the President's New Freedom Commis-sion on Mental Health issued a report titled Achieving the Prom-ise: Transforming Mental Health Care in America. The report rec-ommends that "a new set of diagnostic categories" be developed "to describe and categorize mental disorders in ways that are more scientifically valid and clinically useful." On 23 February 2007, Dr. Steven E. Hyman, Director of the National Institute of Mental Health, agreed with this recommendation in testimony before the Senate Subcommittee on Labor, Health and Human Services, and Education. The scientific validity of a new diagnos-tic category would be increased if it had diagnostic criteria that are more precise than the current DSM-IV PTSD diagnostic criteria.

A critical review was conducted by a group of prominent experts who have carefully weighed the costs and benefits associated with the inclusion of this disorder in the next edition of the Diagnostic and Statistical Manual (DSM). The association between PTSD and aggressive behavior may have been underreported in previous studies, particularly given the heterogeneous nature of the populations studied (i.e., emergency room populations vs. community samples). It also found that "for some individuals with PTSD, an aggressive response following exposure to trauma may be an adaptive response to trauma" and that "aggression may be viewed as a means of coping with abnormal arousal in cases where coping skills are inadequate or ineffective." A study also suggested that research into this association needs to consider interpersonal and intrapersonal factors, such as attachment style and personality traits. The study indicated that "there is a substantial need for an empirically validated conceptualization of aggression in PTSD that allows for variability in aggressive responses across persons."

Clinicians have developed the National Child Traumatic Stress Network (NCTSN) Guidelines for Treating Dissociative Disorders and Traumatic Stress, researchers, and other professionals involved with the care of children and adolescents with traumatic stress. They describe what is known about practical treatment approaches to promote recovery from childhood exposure to trauma or other potentially traumatic events. The Guidelines include information on the types of symptoms typically seen in dissociative disorders and a list of common triggers that may activate dissociative responses. The Guidelines provide recommendations for assessing, diagnosing, and treating traumatic stress disorders among children and adolescents. They discuss various aspects of these disorders, including their theoretical underpinnings and etiology; assessment strategies; the role of social and cultural factors in their development; treatments that can be useful in promoting recovery; types, duration, goals, and course of treatment outcomes; adverse effects to avoid; various forms (e.g., pharmacologic) currently available or may become available in the future; resources available to help clinicians learn more about these topics.

The latest diagnostic manual was released on May 18, 2013. The DSM-5 contains 300 new diagnoses and updates to existing disorders. It introduces new research-based tools to help clinicians predict which individuals may develop mental illnesses over time. The DSM-5 is the product of a workgroup of 1350 APA professionals who sought input from more than 61,500 people, including patients, families, and caregivers; experts in mental health and related disorders; researchers in the substance abuse, addictions, and eating disorders fields; community leaders; and other members of the public.

There was a two-day workshop on 5 November 2011 at the Walter Reed National Military Medical Center (WRNMMC). It was designed to allow clinicians to review current treatment options for PTSD while participating in discussions regarding changes proposed for PTSD criteria in DSM-5. Clinical presentations reviewed included the course of PTSD in children and the use of physiologic measures to assist in diagnosing PTSD, and increasing prevalence rates of PTSD over time.

The workshop was taken by clinicians and other mental health professionals presenting a range of clinical topics. Several military physicians and others were given Lectures that had been directly involved with developing the criteria for all kinds of trauma, including military combat, trench warfare, bombing raids, hurricanes, earthquakes, and wars. The workshop also included several presentations on treatment strategies currently used to treat those diagnosed with PTSD. The workshop also considered the impact that DSM-5 changes could have on military populations and assumed a new diagnosis range.

A total of 868 clinicians completed a survey about DSM-5 PTSD criteria. There were several findings of interest concerning the proposed changes. For example, a study published in April 2015 examined one specific proposed change: inclusion of hyperarousal symptoms as a distinct diagnostic symptom set. The study found that among individuals with PTSD, greater clinician certainty regarding specific hyperarousal symptoms was associated with better self-reported quality of life, lower depression severity, lower alcohol consumption, and more remarkable PTSD improvement.

There are many resources available that provide information about PTSD. Both the Department of Veterans Affairs and the United States Department of Defense (DOD) have established programs to help service members and veterans with PTSD. The VA's National Center for PTSD has information about up-to-date research, treatment options, and evidence-based practices for those who have PTSD, among other resources. DOD provides an array of resources for service members, veterans, their families, and friends, including information on the diagnosis and treatment of PTSD. Several organizations also facilitate communication between military personnel, veterans, their families, and friends by bringing attention to this disorder through public awareness campaigns.

Chapter 1
What is Complex Post-Traumatic Stress Disorder?

C omplex PTSD pertains to individuals who have been exposed to trauma cope with the adverse effects that have occurred as a result of the traumatic event. The disorder affects men and women differently as well as in different ways. Men are more likely to seek help for their problems, but women are more likely to acknowledge if they have complex PTSD because they are typically those who suffer from it. Women are also more willing to discuss their feelings about their traumatic experiences rather than just ignore them.

Many people experience traumatic experiences during their lifetimes, such as accidents, wars, or assaults. For most people, these events are overcome, and in time, they can lead a primarily everyday life. However, some people who endure these types of activities develop post-traumatic stress disorder (PTSD) with symptoms that include flashbacks and nightmares. Other common symptoms are emotional numbness, avoidance of trauma-related thoughts or reminders, feeling irritable or angry for no reason, and feeling guilty that you survived the event while others did not. If a single event causes your PTSD, it's called acute PTSD; if it's been present for more than six months, it may be referred to as chronic PTSD.

PTSD results from a shock or an overwhelming experience that is intense and threatening, causing fear or terror. PTSD is not limited to veterans; anyone can develop PTSD after trauma, even if they were not directly in harm's way. Traumatic events can cause trauma survivors to feel as though they are reliving the traumatic experience repeatedly, leading to feelings of isolation and depression.

Complex PTSD (C-PTSD) is a condition that can develop in people who have endured prolonged or repeated trauma that began in childhood and continues into adult life. These experiences can lead to dissociative disorders, post-traumatic stress disorder, depression, anxiety disorders, and attachment problems.

Complex post-traumatic stress disorder (C-PTSD) is a recently recognized mental health condition resulting from direct or indirect exposure to one or more traumatic events. It is not the same as PTSD because those who develop complex post-traumatic stress lifetime have suffered childhood abuse in addition to an adult trauma, even if it was not recent.

The symptoms of C-PTSD are wide-ranging and are often severe enough to be disabling. They include flashbacks, emotional numbness, severe anxiety, and depression, a sense of a limited future, extreme guilt and shame, psychosomatic physical symptoms such as chronic pain or gastrointestinal disorders; substance abuse problems; anorexia nervosa and bulimia; sexual dysfunctions; suicidal thoughts or attempts; self-injury such as cutting or burning oneself; difficulties with attention or concentration; constantly feeling on guard, irritable or easily startled.

It's also possible to develop PTSD without having experienced a traumatic event. This is called "secondary PTSD." In this case, someone who has already been diagnosed with another condition such as depression, anxiety disorder, bipolar disorder or schizophrenia develops PTSD after experiencing a trauma that would not otherwise have resulted in the development of PTSD alone. For example, a child who experiences depression could develop PTSD after being bullied at school or teased by peers.

The prevalence of C-PTSD is unknown. It is likely underdiagnosed because it can be confused with several other conditions, including PTSD (if the trauma was adult) and borderline personality disorder (if the trauma was childhood). However, the core symptoms of C-PTSD are more long-lasting and far more severe than the symptoms of either PTSD or borderline personality disorder.

PTSD is a severe, chronic, and often debilitating psychiatric disorder characterized by intrusive memories of the traumatic event (e.g., a surprise attack, intruding images), avoidance of reminders that might lead to re-experiencing symptoms (e.g., being at risk of being harmed again), heightened arousal that interferes with sleep and many other emotional responses that result in an inability to function correctly (e.g., avoidance of places, people and activities that a person may have been exposed to during the traumatic event). The PTSD symptom complex is associated with many other psychiatric disorders such as depression, anxiety, personality disorders, substance abuse problems, and serious suicidal thoughts.

Complex post-traumatic stress disorder (C-PTSD) results from long-term chronic exposure to traumatic events. It was first introduced in 2007 by Dr. Charles R. Figley, the Tulane School of Social Work Research Center for Traumatic Stress.

A lot of different types of traumatic events can cause C-PTSD, including war, rape, domestic violence, living with parents who are severely alcoholic or addicted to drugs, and other potentially traumatic situations such as natural disasters or accidents that have occurred while you were helpless or powerless to stop them.

To be diagnosed with C-PTSD, the traumatic event or events must have happened repeatedly over long periods. It is not enough for you to have experienced a single trauma incident - the disorder must involve repeated exposure to trauma over an extended period. It can be hard to know whether you are suffering from C-PTSD. It may take some time for the symptoms of complex PTSD to become apparent, but they will eventually emerge in the form of flashbacks, nightmares, and dissociation. Some people with this condition develop anxiety disorders such as panic attacks and agoraphobia. They may also suffer from depression.

Symptoms
The symptoms are described as follows: The effects of C-PTSD can be devastating. It is as disabling as major depression, with a

prevalence equal to or greater than that of PTSD. Suicide is reported in 10–15% of patients with this condition. The condition is unrecognized mainly by mental health professionals, who may mistake it for other conditions such as borderline personality disorder. It is also under-diagnosed in substance abuse clinics, where it may be misdiagnosed as a substance abuse disorder and then treated with medications rather than psychotherapy.

The symptoms of C-PTSD were described initially in the late 1980s by Dr. Edna Foa. Other studies have backed up her findings, indicating that people who suffer from C-PTSD are more likely to experience depression and anxiety disorders than the general population. Besides, those who develop this condition are often unable to recover from it. This is because people who suffer from C-PTSD have generally been abused at a very young age, which can cause problems with emotional regulation. Besides, C-PTSD is more likely to occur in those who have experienced other traumatic events in their lifetime (including the possibility that resulted in PTSD) and those with histories of ongoing childhood abuse.

Finally, those who experience childhood trauma are particularly at risk for developing C-PTSD because such trauma may cause the child to feel isolated and unable to create healthy social relationships or trust. This isolates them further and makes it difficult for them to find support once they are older.

C-PTSD can be treated with psychotherapy. Specifically, it can be treated with Cognitive Behavioral Therapy, a type of psychotherapy that focuses on changing negative thought patterns and behaviors. The patient must also be able to trust their therapist to form a therapeutic relationship. Those suffering from C-PTSD are often unable to trust others, as they feel as though they have been betrayed by those who were supposed to protect them.

In addition to therapy, many patients are also given medication to treat additional symptoms of anxiety and depression. Because of the high rate of suicidal thoughts associated with C-PTSD, some patients may be prescribed antipsychotic drugs or antidepressants. This is the treatment for both PTSD and the C-PTSD itself.

The underlying causes of complex post-traumatic stress disorder are unclear. It may be complicated by factors such as childhood physical and sexual abuse. There is a genetic component, and childhood abuse has been found to increase the risk of developing PTSD in adulthood.

It has been theorized that those who have a history of being abused while growing up can develop a form of "learned helplessness." Such individuals may come to believe there is no point in trying to stop the abuse, or they may start to think that they cannot control it and, therefore, must endure it. Some people believe that this may be a form of Stockholm syndrome, in which hostages develop a bond with their captors and cooperate with them rather than trying to escape.

There are also theories concerning the genetic component of C-PTSD. One such theory states that genetically predisposed to developing C-PTSD are more likely to experience traumatic events later on in life. The second states that there is little or no genetic component – instead, trauma early on in life is the primary cause of PTSD and C-PTSD.

Post-traumatic stress disorder (PTSD) was first identified in the Diagnostic and Statistical Manual of Mental Disorders III (DSM-III) in 1980 as an anxiety disorder and revised in subsequent diagnostic manuals. Later research showed that PTSD could occur following exposure to a traumatic event. Still, it can also be caused by chronic or isolated exposure to events that do not cause intense fear and horror. Other forms of emotional trauma such as childhood abuse can also lead to PTSD.

The definition of PTSD has changed over time. It was first defined as an anxiety disorder, but it has been classified as an acute stress response starting with the DSM-III-R. It is not considered an anxiety disorder by some researchers. While PTSD has received much attention from the general public, research on this condition lags behind other mental disorders such as depression, alcohol abuse, and substance abuse. Research to develop effective treatments for PTSD have had difficulty in the past, primarily because of a clear definition of the disorder.

DSM classifies many conditions as being related to or causing post-traumatic stress disorder, but it is because these conditions are co-morbid with PTSD that they have been included in the

DSM. PTSD can occur in conjunction with more than one diagnosis, including personality disorders, mood disorders, and other anxiety disorders. Post-traumatic stress disorder can also be caused by exposure to events such as warfare and natural disasters.

A diagnosis of C-PTSD is still being considered for inclusion in the fifth edition of the Diagnostic and Statistical Manual of Mental Disorders (DSM), the American Psychiatric Association's publication used by most psychiatrists worldwide. Because there are no specific diagnostic criteria yet, it may be challenging to receive an official diagnosis from a medical professional. However, many people suffer from C-PTSD that live in your communities and may offer you support and guidance through your journey with this condition.

Posttraumatic stress disorder is diagnosed when you experience symptoms similar to PTSD, but they are caused by exposure to an event or events that have been psychologically devastating for you. must find they are severe enough to interfere with your ability to perform your work, maintain healthy relationships with others, and function in general.

Here are the current diagnostic criteria for PTSD:
Criterion A. Traumatic event: Exposure to actual or threatened death, serious injury, or sexual violence in one (or more) of the following ways
Criterion B. Presence of intrusive symptoms

Criterion C. Difficulty falling or staying asleep. Irritability or out-bursts of anger. Difficulty concentrating. Hypervigilance. Pro-longed and exaggerated startle response.

The National Institute of Mental Health conducted a study in the United States to examine the prevalence of PTSD within the gen-eral population. The results suggested that 13.8% of adults older than 18 had experienced PTSD in their lifetime. According to this study, half of all men and women were likely exposed to trauma during their childhood, but only a fifth of them developed PTSD. The lifetime prevalence rates for post-traumatic stress disorder development due to experiencing individual types of trauma are rape 12.1%, childhood physical abuse 10.2%, and childhood sex-ual abuse 26%. This may be because women are more likely to experience sexual assault and other forms of trauma like rape and domestic violence. It is also suggested that the higher incidence of PTSD in women results from the different ways in which men and women mentally process trauma.

Although many treatments for mental illnesses exist, therapy for PTSD has been inadequately researched. Current therapies in-clude psychological, pharmaceutical, and combined approaches. Several aspects of treatment for PTSD are still being explored and modified, including the length of exposure therapy, the amount of time spent in medicine, and which drugs are given to patients. Edna Foa defines effective exposure therapy as one that causes only temporary discomfort to individuals undergoing it without inducing severe anxiety.

Many PTSD patients have difficulties imagining their trauma outside of real-life experiences, making them want to avoid their traumatic experiences when reliving them in therapy. With imagery rehearsal, patients are asked to repeatedly imagine their traumatic experiences outside of real-life through the use of imagery. Imagery recreating can be done in various ways, including writing narratives, drawing pictures, or using mental images. These techniques are very passive forms of therapy and are often used in combination with other methods.

Exposure therapy is one of the most common PTSD treatments effective for individuals with specific types of trauma who have experienced and remember their trauma vividly. Traditional exposure therapy consists of individuals reliving their trauma while sitting in a safe environment and talking it over with their therapist. The goal is to alleviate anxiety symptoms by bringing back unpleasant memories without inducing the state that initially caused them. To achieve this goal, the individual works with a therapist to create a hierarchy of anxiety-inducing situations and then places as many of those situations in the past as possible.

Chapter 2
Signs of Complex Post-Traumatic Stress Disorder

T he signs that you or someone close to you may have Complex Post-Traumatic Stress Disorder (C-PTSD) can be challenging to identify. Many of the effects of C-PTSD on a person's life are not immediately apparent and often don't surface until months or years after experiencing an event like military combat, physical or sexual abuse, witnessing a shooting, or another horrific event.

Complex post-traumatic stress disorder affects individuals in different ways. However, four main signs could be indicators of complex PTSD. The first is a change in your outward behavior or attitudes, such as overreacting to small objects or increased social withdrawal. Second, the person may have flashbacks or hallucinations of the traumatizing event and has an intense fear this will happen again. Third, nightmares related to the event could be another sign. Lastly, it is common for people to experience solid physical reactions upon exposure to specific reminders of the trauma they faced- such as racing heart rate or difficulty breathing.

A complex PTSD diagnosis is only given when these four signs are present during the disorder. The DSM criteria require that (1) an individual must experience the traumatic event(s); (2) they must be exposed to reminders of it for at least one month or more; (3)

they must exhibit two or more of the following symptoms: Sleep disturbance, trouble concentrating, irritability, emotional detachment, acting out in response to stress, and recurrent distressing recollections of the trauma; (4) there must be a loss in occupational functioning; and (5) there must be a disruption in social relationships.

Many factors can result in complex post-traumatic stress disorder. A trauma that a person of any age experiences can result in complex post-traumatic stress disorder. Most people will share a traumatic event or two throughout their life span. These events can be positive or negative and can profoundly impact an individual's life. A traumatic event that occurs during childhood, adolescence, or early adulthood can profoundly affect the individual's future. For example, someone born into poverty will probably be exposed to different types of trauma throughout their lives. Their home life may be unstable due to poverty, drug abuse, sexual abuse, or domestic violence; they could also become exposed to violent situations such as rape and assault while attending school. Complex post-traumatic stress disorder is a disorder that can disrupt an individual's functionality and ability to function in everyday life.

An individual with complex PTSD may experience any of the following symptoms of this disorder:

Sleep disturbance. This may include a sudden change in the person's sleep patterns, inability to fall asleep, or nightmares about the traumatic event.

Trouble concentrating. This symptom could be shown as changes in performance at work and repeated mistakes and failure due to being overworked or underperforming.

Emotional detachment. The individual can experience this symptom when asked about their traumatic event or their emotional response to it. They can become emotionally detached from other people.

Acting out in response to stress (AOS). This symptom could include high levels of anger, irritability, or problems in interpersonal relationships because they cannot cope with the traumatic memories.

Recurrent distressing memories. This symptom can be experienced frequently by the individual if they have had the same nightmare or flashback recurring for months.

Loss in occupational functioning. People who have complex PTSD may experience a loss of occupational functioning due to poor performance at work and loss of income because they cannot function at work as efficiently as before the trauma occurred. This symptom could also include a decreased ability to participate in social activities due to avoidance of people and places that remind them of what happened to them during their traumatic event(s).

Many treatments can help reduce symptoms of PTSD. The most common one is psychotherapy, and two different types can help women suffering from complex PTSD. Prolonged exposure therapy consists of one-on-one counseling with a professional who could be a psychologist or counselor who will meet with the patient to discuss their traumatic event(s) to reduce reactions to reminders of the event. Trauma-focused cognitive behavioral therapy is similar to prolonged exposure therapy, but it focuses more on changing negative thoughts and feelings related to the traumatic event.

Individuals with complex PTSD may recover from the disorder. However, it is difficult for them and requires a lot of patience. The person must be able to have trust in their therapist and adequately address the trauma with them. They also have to work through their traumatic event issues during their psychotherapy sessions to recover from complex PTSD fully.

These are some of the symptoms and reasons for getting help if you think C-PTSD affects your life. If you have been diagnosed with C-PTSD, this information may provide a starting point for understanding the diagnosis and some resources to help you recover. People with C-PTSD can experience a wide range of symptoms. A diagnosis of C-PTSD does NOT mean that a person has been through the most horrific things that can happen to an individual; it means that they may have experienced chronic trauma in their lives. Someone can experience sexual abuse and domestic violence, but does not have PTSD related to combat or war wounds, so is not likely to meet Complex Post Traumatic Stress Disorder criteria. The key is whether or not a person's symptoms are consistent with what would be expected due to experiencing chronic trauma over periods.

Characteristics of the Disorder

<u>Persistent re-experiencing of the traumatic event.</u> This may look like recurrent memories, nightmares, or flashbacks related to the trauma. Sometimes people with C-PTSD repeatedly act out or play out the trauma in their minds and through their behavior.

<u>Avoidance of stimuli associated with the trauma.</u> This is not necessarily an active avoidance of places or people but can look like a withdrawal from other people and activities that are likely to be associated with thoughts, feelings, and conversations about traumatic events that happened in the past. Sometimes people with C-PTSD may isolate themselves or "shut down" in situations where they anticipate that there will be reminders of the traumatic past.

<u>Persistent symptoms of increased arousal.</u> These will look more like persistent negative beliefs about oneself (i.e., seeing oneself as weak or damaged), others (i.e., seeing others as dangerous), and the world (i.e., believing that "life is not safe"). Also, people with C-PTSD may have difficulty interpreting events accurately. This can look like a distorted interpretation of what has happened and a belief in conspiracy theories.

Negative thoughts about oneself and the world are also not unusual among survivors of trauma. Still, if they persist after months or years of recovery, it can be a strong indicator that someone can have C-PTSD.

The following are some things you can do to determine whether C-PTSD is affecting your life or someone close to you:

- Talk to the person about their experiences in combat and see if they have any symptoms that fit those listed above.
- Ask, "If you *are* experiencing C-PTSD, are you having trouble with people close to you?"
- If the person is not having symptoms that meet the diagnostic criteria for C-PTSD, it does not necessarily mean they are not struggling with something serious.
- Often, a person's struggles after a traumatic event will express themselves in other ways. Suppose the individual is having problems in their relationships and emotional reactions that persist over time.
- Traumatic experiences often negatively affect people's ability to manage anger and regulate intense emotions (e.g., anxiety, sadness, or anger). If the individual is also experiencing problems with anger and strong emotions, these may be symptoms of C-PTSD.
- If the person is also experiencing problems with relationships and emotional reactions over time, it may also be a good indicator that they experience complex post-traumatic stress disorder.

Coping skills can help someone manage their symptoms. Sadly, many people are reluctant to get help when they have symptoms of C-PTSD. This can prevent them from receiving necessary help in managing their symptoms and preventing long-term damage to their lives. It can also make it difficult to get a correct diagnosis. Talking with someone who has experience working with individuals who have experienced severe trauma can also help you get better.

Experienced clinicians can help you understand what is happening for you and offer recommendations for getting better from trauma. If the person has been deployed to a combat zone, they will likely experience complex post-traumatic stress disorder. The symptoms listed in the above description are common to many different types of trauma. Suppose the person is experiencing C-PTSD and experiences problems when attempting to describe their experiences.

Suppose the person is not having symptoms that meet the diagnostic criteria for complex post-traumatic stress disorder. In that case, it does not necessarily mean that they are not struggling with something serious. Often, a person's struggles after a traumatic event will express themselves in other ways. Suppose the individual is having problems in their relationships and emotional reactions that persist over time. In that case, these can be good indicators that they are suffering from trauma as well.

The best treatment for C-PTSD is cognitive-behavioral therapy (CBT). CBT helps people identify and change harmful or negative thoughts by identifying and reframing negative thoughts, thinking errors, and maladaptive thinking styles.

Some signs will continue to persist for many years, and healing may not fully occur until they reach their 50s or beyond. A profound change in your emotional state can occur when you experience complex post-traumatic stress disorder. This type of recovery can leave you feeling exhilarated, liberated, and empowered. You will likely grow in ways you never thought possible while experiencing complex post-traumatic stress disorder.

Complex-PTSD is common in those who have been in combat, but it can also affect people of all backgrounds. Complex Post-Traumatic Stress Disorder (C-PTSD) can be present even if you haven't seen any action or traumatic event. It is less understood than PTSD and yet more common, affecting an estimated 6% population. It is a form of Post-Traumatic Stress Disorder, but it is much more challenging to treat.

Characteristics of Complex PTSD include dissociation, alternating states of hypervigilance (feeling on edge) and numbing (being shut down), depression, and anxiety. The trauma experienced with C-PTSD can be regularly or a singular event that was at the same time violent or sexual. Examples are childhood abuse, rape, domestic violence, kidnapping, torture, and hostage situations.

Some people who have experienced trauma can feel they have lost their sense of self after the event(s). It can be difficult for them to experience pleasure in things they used to enjoy doing. They can feel hopeless about their future. Even when they are not thinking of the event, their body reacts as if they are reliving it.

The most common response to trauma is to have the event affect your behavior and beliefs, which cause you to act differently. Those actions are much more robust for people with C-PTSD and are present in many parts of their lives.

Chapter 3
Complications Associated with Complex PTSD

P ost-traumatic stress disorder (PTSD) is known to have several causes, such as military combat or sexual assault. However, it can also be associated with traumatic events that were ongoing throughout a long period and may have been primarily internalized. People who experience this type of PTSD may not need a single moment to remember their trauma; the triggers might happen gradually over time compared to sudden shocks like those in other types of PTSD.

One way in which this form differs from other types is that re-experiencing symptoms are typically continual rather than being sequential and occasional with periods in between them. These types of signs are not apparent as PTSD develops. For some people, these symptoms might be noticeable in retrospect or before a diagnosis, but for others, they can become evident only after a long period. Complications associated with this type of PTSD include depression and suicidal thoughts.

What are the complications associated with complex PTSD?

It's important to understand that while any traumatized person can experience symptoms similar to those of a diagnosis within the PTSD spectrum, not all symptoms are present in every case. One way this is manifested in complex PTSD is through experiencing traumatic stress reactions over an extended period. This reaction may find different expression methods, including attachment and intimacy, sexual problems, eating disorders, and substance abuse. There may also be persistent feelings of hopelessness or endless despair, difficulty characterizing oneself as a victim (rather than a perpetrator), and dissociative episodes (dissociated memories).

Many people experience trauma over a long period without knowing it. The symptoms may not have been noted as priorities because they were continuous and felt like normal behaviors to those who suffered from the trauma. Because re-experiencing symptoms are ongoing and can be gradual, there is no precise cut moment when one becomes able to recall them as symptomatic or re-experiencing them fully. Some people only become able to identify when re-experiencing is happening again after leaving the situation that caused the trauma.

In addition to these symptoms, it is essential to note that comorbid conditions can complicate any other type of PTSD. Still, this type may be especially likely to develop in these situations. In this case, the diagnosis of complex PTSD is not made at the exclusion of other disorders. Instead, it describes how symptoms from one infection interact with symptoms from another condition due to external factors. People who experience complicated PTSD often report self-medication through various drug and alcohol abuse or eating disorders.

Another disorder associated with trauma is dissociation. Dissociation is when a person's awareness separates from their surroundings to cope with traumatic events and other stressful experiences. It can cause memory loss and feelings of detachment. It is sometimes referred to as the "frozen" state when a person is in complete denial that the traumatic event has happened. Once the dissociation has subsided, there may be flashbacks or nightmares from that time with no recall of what happened.

Disassociative Identity Disorder is a condition where the personality of the person changes. It is a coping mechanism for the person to deal with the immense pain and emotional trauma they have been through. It can also explain why some people experience sudden mood swings or emotional outbursts. While one personality may be experiencing emotions such as anger or sadness, another character may be feeling different emotions at that time. These changes in identity can cause profound confusion and instability in social settings, which further compounds the person's complex issues.

Complex PTSD will often continue until there is a stable psychiatric diagnosis. Many of these people often first report their trauma in flashbacks and may have many unusual symptoms or memories regarding the traumatic event. The nature of these memories can be entirely realistic and maybe very vivid in some cases, but they will only become particularly noticeable after time passes.

The defining characteristic of complicated PTSD is when re-experiencing is not always present but has begun to occur again after a long absence from the traumatic event or situation that caused it. The symptoms may appear and then disappear, leading to a pattern of flashbacks that can commonly be mistaken for other types of PTSD. This pattern is sometimes associated with ongoing traumatic events and involves emotional abuse or neglect during childhood.

Complex PTSD was initially described by Judith Herman M.D, a feminist psychiatrist who wrote about its prevalence in women who have experienced physical or sexual abuse throughout their lives. Her description was based on several case studies, her own experiences with women in therapy sessions, and PTSD research on male and female soldiers from World War II.

It is important to note that not everyone with a traumatic event in their history will experience this type of PTSD. The symptoms of the other types may be more severe or may be present before the trauma. This definition was removed in the DSM-5 (2013), and some now consider complex PTSD to be a spectrum disorder along with other related conditions such as borderline personality disorder.

People with complex PTSD suffer from extremely vivid memories and often say that they cannot forget the events they experienced. They also report re-experiencing symptoms such as emotional numbness or dissociation, mainly when reminders of the stressful event are present (such as hearing someone speak or seeing someone from the traumatic event).

While people living with simple PTSD tend to experience significant anxiety and often have flashbacks upon re-arriving at a stressful place, people with complicated PTSD typically experience emotional numbness. People may have a feeling of "not caring" or inadequacy regarding the traumatic event. This can also cause an inability to correctly remember the event, making it harder to work with a therapist or other healthcare professionals. People may also report that they were not surprised by the stressful event because they had felt something terrible was going to happen.

However, some people report being aware of what might happen in the traumatic situation before it happened. These individuals may have a feeling of resignation about whatever is about to occur.

The symptoms of complicated PTSD include:

These symptoms contrast to PTSD symptoms such as fear and anxiety and avoidance of particular places or emotions with simple PTSD. Complex PTSD can sometimes be a diagnosis for people who have other psychiatric disorders. In particular, borderline personality disorder or major depressive disorder can cause re-experiencing of previously suppressed memories. Additionally, some people may experience complicated PTSD after experiencing the symptoms of another mental disease, making the diagnosis confusing and challenging to identify. These individuals may be particularly likely to develop stress disorders and are at higher risk for several physical illnesses due to being chronically ill and having a high level of chronic stress.

People with complicated PTSD have difficulty emotionally regulating their feelings and often report an inability to feel anger or sadness accurately. This may occur because they feel disconnected from their emotions and not able to express them fully. They may also feel as if they have no control over their thoughts and feelings, leading to suicidal thoughts.

People with complicated PTSD often experience difficulties in social relationships because of the emotional numbness during a stressful situation. They may also avoid social problems due to the potential re-experiencing of memories or the emotional numbness through social interactions. This is especially common among people with complex PTSD who have grown up in homes that were violent or traumatic, had abandoned them, or where familial abuse was present throughout their childhoods.

The most commonly reported main issues for the participants were distrust, depression, and anxiety. These symptoms are consistent with Complex PTSD and explain why many people have difficulty managing day-to-day tasks like getting out of bed or working. They also report feeling extreme amounts of emotional pain as if something is 'trapped' inside them which they cannot get out of. Many participants also identified feeling helpless and worthless. These symptoms seem to be similarly consistent with Complex PTSD, which can be explained by seeing their lives as filled with emotional pain and trauma that they cannot escape.

Complex PTSD is similar to Post-Traumatic Stress Disorder (PTSD), a disorder that occurs due to prolonged and repeated trauma in the lives of some individuals. Though not all people who have experienced complex trauma develop Complex PTSD, in many cases, some symptoms occur for the individual suffering from Complex PTSD—disorder—that may lead to other mental health disorders. Someone who has experienced Complex PTSD could develop Posttraumatic Stress Symptoms, for example, anxiety, depression, relationship problems, a lack of purpose in life, lowered self-esteem, and difficulty dealing with change.

Differences can be found between PTSD and Complex PTSD in that with a disorder such as PTSD, and an event must be severely traumatic to result in these symptoms. What is often not explained is that not all people who have experienced trauma or abuse will experience complex symptoms as well; some individuals may only have severe symptoms if their trauma has been complicated to experience or if they have experienced it very recently. One of the most significant ways that Complex PTSD differs from PTSD is that Complex PTSD symptoms can result from many different traumatic events and abuses.

Complex PTSD also has similarities with other conditions such as Borderline Personality Disorder (BPD). Both have symptoms that include difficulties in forming close relationships, self-harm behavior, a lack of empathy, and difficulty regulating emotions. An individual with Complex PTSD may experience symptoms similar to BPD. This could be because their abuse has resulted in them becoming distrustful of others, having been unable to form an attachment with anyone, and changing their outlook on people around them.

Complex trauma is not diagnosed during childhood; however, the symptoms can be noticed as early as adulthood due to complications during adolescence and adulthood. All victims of complex trauma suffer in very different ways, but all will have some similarities in their manifestations. These manifestations are as follows:

Complex PTSD symptoms include mood swings, loss of emotions, difficulties in relationships, insomnia, feelings of persecution, and self-loathing. Some people have thoughts about harming themselves because they feel that they have no control over their lives. Also, fear of being alone and fear of abandonment are common disorders. These actions can cause people to lose motivation in life because they feel nothing for the future. Some people choose to end their lives due to the effects a complex trauma holds over them.

Complex PTSD and depression are often linked together. Depression can be connected to the effects of abuse, neglect, and traumatic experiences. Symptoms of depression include the inability to experience pleasure, loss of appetite or overeating, insomnia, irritability or crying for no reason, feelings of hopelessness, and thoughts about harming or hurting oneself.

The effects of complex trauma may last forever, but there are ways to manage this complex trauma and allow individuals with Complex PTSD to regain some sense of control over their lives. Therapy can help people with Complex PTSD gain control over their emotions, thoughts, and actions. The treatment for complex trauma requires more than one form of treatment. It is a partnership between the person coping with complex trauma and the therapist to regain a sense of control over what happened to them and gain the tools needed to live long, happy lives.

Chapter 4
Treating Complex Post-Traumatic Stress Disorder

T he most well-studied treatment is Cognitive Behavioral Therapy (CBT). CBT includes teaching you skills to manage your thoughts and feelings, and behaviors. As well, medication may be prescribed to help relieve symptoms. We all experience traumatic events, from being bullied at school to losing a loved one. You may notice feelings of apprehension or fear when faced with something that reminds you about the actual event.

Complex Post-Traumatic Stress Disorder (C-PTSD) is a form of PTSD that develops in specific situations where the victim has experienced ongoing trauma, such as with captives and conflict victims. Victims may also develop C-PTSD if they have experienced physical violence or sexual abuse in addition to emotional trauma. C-PTSD sufferers may have some difficulties related to guilt, shame, anger, and aggression.

Symptoms of Complex Post Traumatic Stress Disorder can be treated with psychotherapy aimed at changing behavior and thought patterns that lead to self-destructive behaviors such as rage attacks or addictions in combination with medication when needed.

The following symptoms are required for the diagnosis of C-PTSD:

- Persistent enduring effects on functioning in one or more major areas of life such as work, family relations, other interpersonal relationships, and self-perception, beginning or worsening after the exposure to trauma.
- Impaired ability to regulate emotions after being exposed to traumatic stressors.
- Intolerance of being alone or separation from others after traumatic stressors This can be evidenced by avoidance of situations in which others are present to be alone, e.g., workplace, family gatherings, or parties); and feeling that one must stay close to other people (e.g., spouse) even when there are no threats present.
- Prolonged exposure: PTSD causes anxiety about things that remind you about the original trauma. If this describes you, a good treatment option is prolonged exposure therapy. This involves gradually and repeatedly exposing yourself to the perceived trigger of your PTSD.

Treatments

Effective treatments are available, and research is being done to improve treatments. Doctors typically recommend that people with PTSD see a doctor who understands the long-term effects of this condition and can offer them the most effective treatment they need. Traumatic brain injury (TBI) and other physical conditions may also contribute to the symptoms of this condition, so it's essential to see a doctor find the best approach for your diagnosis.

Eye movements and EMDR: Eye Movement Desensitization Reprocessing (EMDR) is a therapy that involves looking at specific memories and emotions to aid your recovery. The way EMDR works is that you imagine yourself back in the situation that you find difficult. You then move your eyes rapidly across a screen, trying to move forward through the memory without going back to the past. The point of this exercise is to expose yourself to the triggering event repeatedly until it no longer makes you anxious.

Cognitive behavioral therapy: This therapy focuses on helping people who feel anxious or distressed develop their feelings using behavioral techniques. Also known as Behaviour Therapy, this type of therapy is often seen as the most effective. CBT often seeks the root cause of the distress in your life that may be causing or worsening post-traumatic stress disorder symptoms. Treatments must seek to find the underlining reasons for PCSD so they can work out what's stopping healing from occurring naturally on its own.

CBT is very effective for treating Post Traumatic Stress Disorder. One study that tested out CBT found that 84% of people who completed treatment were free of their symptoms.

Cognitive therapy: When faced with distressing memories, some people may find that talking to a therapist about their experiences can help them relive the situation and accept its painful aspects, making it easier to move forward. This form of therapy focuses on your thoughts and emotions as well as physical sensations and reactions.

Medication: Medications are not a substitute for seeing a doctor for your mental health, but they can help you manage symptoms effectively enough to live a healthy life. Medications are used to treat post-traumatic stress disorder and other conditions related to long-term stress, such as chronic pain or depression. They work by regulating chemicals in your brain that relate to emotional responses, particularly chronic stress.

People often feel ashamed of their mental health and don't want to be seen as weak. Anxiety can make you feel like you have nothing to offer the world, that you are a burden, so it's essential to recognize that there is a mental illness, and most people are dealing with it in one way or another.

Don't be afraid to seek professional help. The stigma around mental health is reducing all the time, but it's not entirely gone yet, so it's important to remember that millions of people in this country need support no matter how they feel about asking for help. If you're struggling with your mental health, don't be afraid to ask for help. If you don't feel like you can tell anyone about your struggles, talk to someone anonymously.

These treatments are still relatively new, and thus, need more research to be fully understood before they can become a treatment for everyone. This is not to say that treatments for PTSD do not exist. If you feel like you may have PTSD, it's essential to under-stand the differences between PTSD and a normal stress reaction. Complex PTSD is increasingly recognized as a mental health con-dition and should be treated accordingly. The DSM 5 has outlined guidelines for diagnosing and treating complex PTSD, with spe-cific recommendations for the treatment of Complex PTSD.

Now, let's review the basics of post-traumatic stress disorder (PTSD) and how it affects someone's life. At its root, PTSD is an anxiety disorder that involves recurrent and intrusive thoughts, images, or memories of the traumatic event. These often lead to powerful feelings of shame or guilt, severe anxiety symptoms (such as flashbacks), avoidance behaviors, and difficulty concen-trating on work or school tasks.

Many individuals with this type of anxiety disorder also experi-ence depression, anger, insomnia, dissociation, and irritability. Clinicians use the PTSD checklist to diagnose patients. This test correlates with the clinician's judgment of a patient's ability to function. Symptoms usually last a few months and resolve grad-ually over time.

The good news is that attention to treatment can help many peo-ple cope with PTSD symptoms in the long run. Suppose you have experienced an extremely traumatic event. In that case, your doc-tor may prescribe medications that can combat some of your symptoms to help alleviate anxiety and other intrusive thoughts associated with PTSD. Some victims may need therapy to get past their trauma and learn how to live their lives again in a healthy manner.

Complex post-traumatic stress disorder is a condition that requires understanding and treatment. The National Center for PTSD says that complex post-traumatic stress disorder is "...a severe and chronic condition that can be debilitating. People who have been traumatized often suffer subsequent losses, such as of the sense of safety and security, control, trust, and self-esteem." This comes from the fact that the traumatic event alters your brain chemistry so that it becomes difficult to cope with real-life circumstances. In other words, it's a mental illness...no one chooses to have.

Complex PTSD is not a simple disorder that can be diagnosed as, "Oh, you just need some time to heal and move past your trauma." It is a disorder that requires time and attention to heal. The stress of the past event can cause chronic physical symptoms such as headaches, stomach pains, or insomnia. Stress also contributes significantly to physical problems such as high blood pressure, heart disease, or depression.

For this reason, many complex post-traumatic stress disorder patients are recommended to see a physician who specializes in treating mental illnesses for guidance and treatment planning. Psychotherapy is often a primary or adjunct treatment for many people with PTSD.

The types of psychotherapy used to treat PTSD are varied, but they usually fall into two categories. The first kind of therapy to help someone who has PTSD is called exposure therapy. This type of therapy helps patients confront their anxiety symptoms by exposing them to the things they fear. So, suppose, for example, a person is diagnosed with PTSD after witnessing an automobile accident. In that case, they might be exposed to traffic as a treatment to conquer their fears and anxiety about the situation. It's a pretty straightforward technique.

The second kind of psychotherapy commonly used to treat PTSD is cognitive restructuring. In this type of treatment, patients talk with their therapist about how they view the world and how they react to people, situations, or events. These conversations allow them to take a more proactive or aggressive role in their treatment plan and life. They get to choose how they live their lives...not some past event that affects their everyday life.

Well, you need to understand that you are not your illness! You have suffered an event that has changed who you are...but you are still here living in the present...not the past! The critical thing to remember is that your life is very much worth living. You are not alone in your battle. You can overcome these symptoms and allow you to live your life as you see fit! This is possible if you are willing to work hard and build a strong support network of friends, family, or professionals who can help keep your mind, body, and spirit in balance.

Traumatic events can include military combat, violent personal assaults, natural disasters, and terrorist attacks. Symptoms of PTSD can be severe enough to prevent victims from living their lives and enjoying their time with others. It's an ongoing battle for all those affected by this horrific illness to find effective treatments for their symptoms without putting themselves at risk of addiction or other adverse consequences of medications.

Chapter 5
Therapy for Complex PTSD

C omplex PTSD or C-PTSD is a condition that affects people who have survived prolonged and repeated trauma in their life. It used to be called Disorders of Extreme Stress (DESNOS) and can happen to anyone who has experienced prolonged trauma in different ways.

The question on many people's minds is: why? Why put themselves through such an experience to recover from the pain of the past? There are many reasons people find therapy so helpful. Therapy can help us relieve stress, release anger, face our fears, and take control of our lives once more. It can be an opportunity to learn more about the self.

To begin, therapy is an incredibly safe environment in which to face our fears. Oftentimes, people who have PTSD experience a heightened sense of awareness and anxiety concerning the things they fear. Therapy allows you to confront these fears in a safe manner and work through them. You will be able to see if there are any inaccuracies related to your worries. You will also be able to determine whether or not your views are beneficial or detrimental.

There are two ways in which therapy for complex PTSD can help you confront fears: gradual exposure and cognitive restructuring. Gradual exposure introduces a trauma memory and gradually increases the amount of time spent with it. The goal is to build your tolerance as to the amount of time you can spend with the memory before you become triggered to decrease the anxiety that comes with each exposure. In cognitive restructuring, one works through their trauma by identifying unrealistic beliefs about their situation and replacing them with more realistic thoughts.

Another way therapy helps people is to remove the fear that springs up when they discuss their experiences. When you talk about your past experiences or even bring up memories you associate with those experiences, some people fear response that increases their physical anxiety.

When you bring up a memory associated with your trauma, it can appear in your mind like you are re-experiencing the traumatic event all over again. You may have been able to handle this fear in the past, but now that you are open to talking about your experience, it has become present. Some people find that they can talk about traumatic experiences more efficiently and with less fear after they have been through therapy.

However, complex PTSD is also a severe condition and needs to be treated as such. The following article will cover some of the C-PTSD symptoms and how therapists can work with these individuals.

The symptoms of complex PTSD can seem to be a catch-all diagnosis that encompasses any traumatic experience. We should not forget that this is a rare occurrence. The vast majority of people diagnosed with trauma-related stress will never experience a diagnosis of complex PTSD. We should remember this as we understand how they differ from those who do.

As stated before, many people experience high amounts of stress after suffering the loss of loved ones or those close to them. Those who have suffered trauma will often follow the initial events and events during the time they were recovering by reliving them repeatedly through their minds. This is a process called "neuroplasticity" and can be explained best as an event in which one's brain 'rewires' itself to form new connections or learning. In those with complex PTSD, it is still possible to create new relationships, but because of the intense and repeated experience of trauma, the memory itself has become "hard-wired."

The role that memory plays in these disorders will vary from person to person. Some people create compounding triggers by separating themselves from others or places where they feel safe and have experienced past trauma due to their PTSD. Even environments that are not directly dangerous can be triggering for those with these disorders. When a person is started, stress hormones such as cortisol are released into the brain, which may cause sleep disturbances and difficulty concentrating. For those with severe PTSD, the triggers may increase their anxiety and make them feel as if they are "walking through a minefield."

This experience is commonly referred to as hypervigilance. Hypervigilance can cause many issues, including obstructive visual scanning, inability to focus or relate to people, paranoia, and fear of abandonment. This disorder can cause secondary symptoms like depression or substance abuse due to the constant sense of threat and isolation. Hypervigilance often leads to the misattribution of thoughts, which certain events can cause. For example, a person may become convinced that they are being followed or watched at all times when they are alone in their home. They may become convinced they are "being judged" or that "everyone is staring at them".

Compounding trauma is when one's mind has been triggered by a past traumatic event in which they were aware during the actual event itself. This usually occurs when people have already been diagnosed with PTSD but are also dealing with another type of stress, such as substance abuse or depression. A person may drink alcohol to feel calm while remembering the traumatic event without remembering any details about it afterward.

In some cases, it can be a way to try and deal with the symptoms at hand.

Lastly, trauma-related dissociation is when there is a disconnection between the present and past by simply forgetting what happened. This usually occurs when there are only minor triggers in the present that remind the person of their trauma. However, this does not always work, and many people find that they will have traumatic effects on events in their lives based on their current level of distress by recalling past events.

Understanding these disorders can help us understand how therapists can help others with complex PTSD. One of the main goals of therapy commonly used to treat PTSD is to reduce anxiety and these other symptoms. It seems that this can be achieved through exposure therapy. In a safe environment, the person with the disorder is exposed to traumatic experiences and guided through them by talking about them. One way that therapists can validate someone's experience is by telling them a similar story.

Another important goal of therapy is to help people manage their actions based on their current emotional state, rather than being controlled by emotions such as mood or stress. Teaching skills can achieve this in relaxation and meditation, which help people become more aware of their inner thoughts and feelings.

This may be useful when dealing with a particularly traumatic event such as the death of a loved one. This can manifest itself in many ways: the survivor may constantly become on guard, easily startled or irritated at the minor things, or struggle with insomnia and nightmares.

For some sufferers, these symptoms may go on for years following the trauma and leave them living in a never-ending nightmare with no escape; but there is hope. Knowledge of PTSD's existence has led to an increased understanding by mental health professionals that not everyone responds to therapy in the same way. Today, various treatment methods are available for those battling complex PTSD shown to have immense benefits.

Complex PTSD is a relatively new diagnosis used to describe the mental condition of people who have experienced prolonged trauma. It's different from post-traumatic stress disorder in that it encompasses a broader range of symptoms and behaviors.

There are three main types of therapy for Complex PTSD, including psychotherapy, which can help improve moods, sleeping habits, and coping mechanisms; EMDR therapy helps patients manage their traumatic events, and talk therapy or counseling. All three methods may incorporate art forms like drawing or painting and group sessions to speak to each other about their traumas.

Additionally, many of the therapies are often very expensive and may only be covered by insurance if you have a designated diagnosis.

The Different Types of Therapy for Complex PTSD

Psychotherapy is designed to help people change unhealthy behaviors and manage their emotions. This type of therapy aims to improve your mental health by exploring how past experiences have affected your behavior in the present. It compares current problems with past abuse, neglect, or trauma that occurred during childhood. Psychotherapy can also help you find new ways to cope with painful memories or emotions and even improve social skills and relationships.

One common type of psychotherapy for Complex PTSD is called cognitive-behavioral therapy (CBT). During this type of treatment, a therapist will work with you to change the negative thoughts and behaviors that may be causing problems in your life.

CBT can help reduce the anger, anxiety, depression, social isolation, and paranoia you may be experiencing due to your traumatic experiences. This makes it especially well-suited for people with mood disorders and those suffering from post-traumatic stress. It helps to identify patterns that have been damaging and replace them with healthy coping mechanisms. The end goal is to help patients live more effectively.

Another type of psychotherapy for Complex PTSD is called dialectical behavior therapy (DBT). This type of therapy was initially used to treat people with eating disorders or suicidal tendencies and was later found to be an effective treatment for PTSD.

DBT focuses on helping patients manage their emotions and develop healthier ways of thinking. In DBT, counselors teach different methods of managing intense situations by changing your perspective or acting in a certain way based on your emotional state. It also focuses on developing and improving relationships with others.

This helps patients learn how to confront their fears in a safe environment and reduce the fear or concern about the trauma.

EMDR therapy is designed to treat PTSD by helping you release the underlying trauma and stress from your past experiences. EMDR combines several different techniques initially developed by doctor Francine Shapiro, who helped victims of war trauma process their memories and hone in on painful memories.

EMDR therapists work with patients who have Complex PTSD by asking them questions about their experiences, then creating a storyboard that includes pictures, symbols, and other details that serve as reminders of the traumatic events.

Talk therapy or counseling is another option for people with Complex PTSD. During this process, a licensed professional will meet with you to talk about your past trauma and help you cope with current stressors in your life.

There are several different kinds of counseling depending on your situation, including family therapy, couples therapy, grief counseling, and group therapy. You may want to discuss how much time should be spent on your past trauma versus other daily stressors with your therapist. It is also important to mention that sometimes medication can be combined with one's therapy to reduce symptoms associated with Complex PTSD and help one manage their mental illness.

One of the first treatments for complex PTSD is psychotherapy. Psychotherapy is a type of counseling in which the therapist listens to the patient and helps him or her cope with emotions, thoughts, and behaviors associated with a traumatic event. Many people who have complex PTSD opt for some form of alternative therapy. Self-help groups are a form of therapy in which individuals share their stories. These groups provide support and education to those who are experiencing complex PTSD.

Many individuals who have complex PTSD opt to engage in spiritual healing techniques, such as meditation or yoga, to cope with their traumas.

Chapter 6
Medication for Complex PTSD

C an you believe that as many as 40% of all Americans deal with mental health issues, and one in six adults will experience brain disease throughout their lifetime? The good news is that there are treatment options available to help. If you're living with complex PTSD, you might be unclear about what specific medications are prescribed to treat this condition. It's not a simple answer since so many different combinations can be specified. With that said, here is a brief overview of some common types of medication:

Medications for Complex PTSD include the following:

— SSRIs (Selective serotonin and norepinephrine reuptake inhibitors) such as Zoloft and Prozac; these medications help people who experience intrusive memories or flashbacks by regulating the overproduction of neurotransmitters in the brain. They also help individuals struggling with depression or anxiety issues due to trauma.

— Antidepressants that boost serotonin levels in the brain include Prozac and Wellbutrin (bupropion); these help patients who experience depression, anxiety, irritability, or impulsivity due to trauma.

— Anticonvulsants such as Neurontin; these medications are prescribed for those struggling with dissociation or severe mood swings related to their trauma experience. These produce a mild sedative effect when taken in larger doses. Neurontin is typically prescribed for those with Post-Traumatic Stress Disorder and Complex PTSD that may cause repetitive, intrusive thoughts or nightmares.

— Antipsychotic medications such as Risperdal, Seroquel, Haldol, and Zyprexa; are typically prescribed for PTSD patients with severe symptoms of dissociation or paranoia related to trauma. These medications are more commonly used for patients with schizophrenia or bipolar disorder.

— Antidepressant/anxiolytics such as Elavil (amitriptyline) and Sinequan (doxepin); these medications help reduce the severity of intrusive thoughts and emotional numbing that is often experienced by people who have been traumatized.

— Anti-anxiety medications such as Ativan (lorazepam), Valium, and Klonopin; reduce anxiety symptoms resulting from trauma, fear, or stress.

— Antipsychotic such as Risperdal, Seroquel, Haldol, and Zyprexa; these can be prescribed for those dealing with obsessive/compulsive behavior due to trauma.

— Benzodiazepines such as Librium, Ativan, and Xanax; these medications help some individuals experiencing dissociative episodes related to trauma. They reduce anxiety and help reduce trauma-induced intrusive thoughts. Thus they are prescribed for dissociation, insomnia and panic attacks.

— Anti-depressants such as Zoloft, Wellbutrin (bupropion), and Cymbalta (duloxetine) are commonly used to treat PTSD patients who are simultaneously struggling with depression or anxiety disorders.

The symptoms of complex PTSD can vary widely from individual to individual. The triggers that lead to reactions or flashbacks may also vary. This means that the list of possible medications for complex PTSD is also very long and includes many different options. The use of drugs can help aid PTSD patients to cope with symptoms, integrating treatments into their daily lives. However, it is not always necessary and should be used in conjunction with other therapies, such as therapy.

The standard treatment for PTSD and complex PTSD is antidepressants, which can help with the mood regulation of patients. These medications help to regulate the HPA axis that is affected by complex PTSD. Shifts in the HPA axis can lead to hyperarousal, which underlies the symptoms of complex PTSD. Antidepressants are also associated with alleviating symptoms of depression and anxiety.

It is not uncommon among patients with complex PTSD to have problems experiencing positive feelings. In light of this, antidepressants can help people who do not seek a standard range of emotions. However, they are less effective than other medications such as SSRIs or SNRIs for treating depression involved with complex PTSD because of their inability to affect the HPA axis.

Chapter 7
Other Ways to Treat Complex Post-Traumatic Stress Disorder

I f you have been diagnosed with complex PTSD, you're not alone, and there are several ways to treat this condition. You will need to see a mental health professional begin any treatment. However, seeking professional guidance is only the first step in a long process, including various medications and psychotherapeutic interventions. It can be a debilitating diagnosis to live with, and many other forms of treatment may provide relief.

We are going to explore some of the treatments for PTSD other than conventional talk therapy and medication. Some people will get relief from physical activity such as yoga, while others may find more success using mindfulness techniques to control their symptoms.

One of the primary forms of treatment for PTSD is talk therapy. This is the most common form of psychotherapy as it is widely available and inexpensive. You can even get this type of treatment reimbursed by your health insurance in most states, which makes it even more accessible.

For many people who have PTSD, in-depth talk therapy is a way to help control their symptoms and live a more fulfilling life. This type of talk therapy will be highly individualized, as every person with PTSD has different triggers, reactions, and symptoms.

There are many forms of talk therapy, and they are sometimes used in combination. The main categories include:

1. Exposure: This approach involves learning to identify and confront a traumatic situation that you find frightening and disturbing so that you can conquer the fear and anxiety it elicits. By engaging the fear while it is present, you learn to resist when the anxiety arises in the future.

2. Compensatory skills: This type of therapy involves identifying problematic behaviors that you use as coping mechanisms for dealing with a trauma or stressful situation. For example, avoiding social problems or seeking reassurance from others when your mind is racing can be used in this way by an individual who has PTSD. The goal is to learn to use healthier coping mechanisms so that the negative behavior becomes unnecessary.

3. Cognitive Behavioral Therapy: This approach seeks to identify patterns of unhelpful thoughts and behavior that set off and worsen the anxiety symptoms of PTSD. It involves developing new coping mechanisms and replacing negative thoughts with more positive ones so that you can be more relaxed and centered when an incident occurs that would previously have triggered your anxiety.

Another form of PTSD treatment is physical activity or exercise. Studies show that regular exercise can help your mood, make you sleep better, increase energy, decrease depression and improve self-confidence. It can also help balance hormones such as cortisol which is essential for emotional wellbeing.

Exercise is the perfect panacea

Many treatment options exist for PTSD, but so far, exercise is one of the most effective ways to treat the disorder. Exercising floods your body with endorphins which are chemicals that transmit signals related to pain relief and pleasure. This makes it possible for your brain to produce natural substances which help fight depression and reduce anxiety levels.

Exercise can also help you to release pent-up negative emotions that are related to your traumatic experience. By pushing your body to work harder than it would usually do, exercise releases these negative emotions as chemical compounds that have been stored in your muscles. This process allows you to feel more optimistic about the future and less likely to be triggered by reminders of the past.

It is essential for you not to push yourself too far when exercising for PTSD, which could lead to physical injuries, making it difficult for you to exercise in the future. By following a supervised exercise program, you will be able to reap all of the benefits of exercising without risking any injuries that could discourage you from continuing with this treatment.

If you have been experiencing PTSD and have tried other methods of treating the disorder with little success, it might be time to consider exercising more regularly. By following a regular exercise program, you could find that your symptoms such as anxiety and depression start to fade away.

In one study on the Beijing 2008 Olympics Games, many people diagnosed with PTSD were given 12 weeks of aerobic exercises three days a week while receiving counseling therapy for their trauma and other mental health issues. The results were encouraging-- more than three-quarters of those who completed the exercise program no longer had PTSD.

Exercise can be done in many forms, such as high-intensity interval training, yoga, and tai chi. One of the most accessible forms of physical activity is walking. Walking for exercise is one of the easiest ways to get the training that will feel good, and it can be done anywhere, whether you live in the city or a rural area. It's also a low-cost way to get physical activity and help reduce depression and anxiety.

Exercise can be a powerful treatment for Complex Post Traumatic Stress Disorder, according to previous studies. For those living with PTSD, exercise can help alleviate some of the debilitating stress symptoms that often result from the anxiety and flashbacks associated with PTSD.

For those living with PTSD, a moderate amount of exercise can help reduce symptoms such as depression, anxiety, and sleep disturbances. According to a study published in the "Redbook" journal, even moderate levels of exercise had beneficial effects on those living with PTSD.

The benefits of exercise for those living with PTSD lie in the release of endorphins and an increased heart rate which helps to distract from intrusive thoughts. Essentially, when you exercise, your body releases dopamine and serotonin that help alleviate depressive symptoms by decreasing negative thoughts and self-criticism while increasing positive feelings.

Furthermore, moderating physical activity may also help to reduce trauma-related nightmares by helping you sleep better overall. This is extremely important for women experiencing PTSD, as sleep deprivation and insomnia are more common in female trauma survivors.

Moderate-intensity exercise can also help reduce the irritability associated with PTSD and improve the ability to concentrate. For men who have more severe symptoms of PTSD, vigorous-intensity training is just as practical as therapy in reducing anxiety and stress.

Research suggests that aerobic exercise and resistance training may help reduce depressive symptoms that often result from the trauma of PTSD. Unless this is life-threatening, modulating physical activity can be a highly effective treatment for PTSD.

There are several reasons why many mental health professionals believe it is an essential condition to study and understand. Because C-PTSD has not been officially recognized, it can be challenging to receive professional treatment for this condition. However, treatment methods can help you cope with complex PTSD or overcome it completely.

You've probably heard of PTSD, but did you know that it can develop in two (or more) ways? There's the more well-known Acute

Stress Disorder, and then there's Complex PTSD. Even if you're not a psychologist, counselor, or mental health professional, this book should be help clear up some misconceptions about what causes C-PTSD and how it can be treated. Learn about treatments like cognitive processing therapy that have been proven to be effective for treating some serious emotional issues.

For more on the definition of Complex Post Traumatic Stress Disorder, or C-PTSD, I recommend checking out an excellent article from the Washington Post. Suffice it to say that since this is one of the most common mental health issues out there, it's essential for people to know about it.

The origins of C-PTSD can be traced back to the events of 9/11. People who were in New York City at the time saw a lot more than they'd expected when those planes hit their city. Understandably, many were left with severe anxiety and trauma in their lives; others had more complicated reactions. Many symptoms of C-PTSD are hypervigilance or being constantly on the lookout for danger. People who suffer from C-PTSD will feel like they're in trouble, even if the situation doesn't necessarily call for it. This is another way this condition differs from PTSD; in PTSD, a person recognizes that a threat or trauma is over and moves past it. A person with C-PTSD relives their experience repeatedly, but they're not going to "get better" like they might in PTSD. C-PTSD can also be complicated by mental illnesses like depression and bipolar disorder, and it can even lead to substance abuse.

This is why there's no "one size fits all" treatment for C-PTSD. People need to seek the help they need to recover from their symptoms, including "talk therapy" or other forms of therapy. Most people probably know CBT is a technique that works well for mental health problems like anxiety, but it's also been shown to treat issues like PTSD and C-PTSD as well. As noted, exercise is vital.

Chapter 8
Complex PTSD in Children and Adolescents

The mental health condition known as Post-Traumatic Stress Disorder (PTSD) has been well-documented in adults. It is a disorder triggered by a traumatic event, such as war, rape, death of family members or loved ones, or other incidents that threaten one's safety. PTSD can involve flashbacks during which the individual relives the traumas experienced and attempts to avoid anything associated with them.

A common question asked is, "Can children get PTSD?" The answer is yes. The youngest person reported to have this condition was just 18 months old. Experiences that are traumatic for a child might not involve physical violence or injury. A child's response to a traumatic event can stem from fear, separation anxiety, or other stress-related reactions. Children exposed to domestic violence, sexual abuse, and parental substance abuse have a higher likelihood of developing PTSD.

Children are also more vulnerable than adults to the marked changes in brain chemistry that occur following trauma, leading to symptoms such as irritability, sleep disturbances, and hypervigilance. Post-traumatic stress disorder can affect children as young as seven years old when they witness a car accident or sexual assault.

It also includes ways to help these young people overcome their symptoms and regain their ability to function normally.

Diagnosis of Post-Traumatic Stress Disorder requires that a child or adolescent has experienced a traumatic event involving actual or threatened death or serious injury or a threat to physical integrity. Symptoms of PTSD can vary significantly from child to child; however, the primary categories are re-experiencing, avoidance and numbing, and hyperarousal.

Symptoms include:

- Recurrent and intrusive thoughts about the traumatic event, including images, opinions, or perceptions.
- Recurrent distressing dreams about the traumatic event. Children may have nightmares or night terrors (waking up in a sweat because they are afraid). They may also talk about dreams that feature themes related to the trauma.
- Acting or feeling as if they were experiencing a traumatic event again (also known as a "flashback").
- Re-experiencing the trauma in the form of physical symptoms (such as headaches, stomach aches, and pains, or feeling sick to their stomach).
- Emotional reactions such as fear, horror, or anger when reminded of traumatic events outside of conscious awareness. These can be triggered by positive or negative experiences that remind them of the original trauma. For ex-

ample, they may have a panic attack when they see someone who looks like someone from the actual traumatic incident.

Everyday thoughts and feelings associated with re-experiencing symptoms include:

- Anger and irritability. These may be expressed through outbursts, temper tantrums, or fighting with siblings or peers at school.
- Anxiety, fear, or insecurity. This may be expressed via separation anxiety or fear of the dark. They may be afraid to go out of the house alone.
- Depression and despair. Children and adolescents with PTSD may have trouble experiencing positive emotions such as happiness and joy. They sometimes use acting-out behaviors to express their depression and despair, including running away from home or fighting with peers at school.
- Avoidance is another set of symptoms that can occur in children and adolescents who develop PTSD. These symptoms may include voiding people, places, activities, or things that were present during the traumatic event.
- Lack of interest or participation in previously meaningful activities. This includes schoolwork, extracurricular activities, and hobbies.

- Problems are concentrating on the tasks they used to enjoy (such as schoolwork).
- Avoidance of certain situations or places associated with their trauma. For example, children who experienced child abuse may avoid their parents and others trying to help them out of fear that they will be hurt again. Children who experience neglect may avoid spending time with their friends to avoid being alone with the parents. Avoidance is widespread among children who experienced sexual abuse as a child.
- Numbing is another set of symptoms that can occur in children and adolescents who develop PTSD. These symptoms may include feeling emotionally numb, disconnected, or estranged.
- Reduced interest in previously enjoyable activities or hobbies. For example, children who get a lot of pleasure from playing video games may lose interest after experiencing trauma. This also may include a loss of interest in making friends or other activities that they previously enjoyed, such as attending school, extracurricular activities, and socializing with family members and peers.
- Feeling detached from their own thoughts and feelings — this is sometimes called "numbing out. " They may feel emotionally flat, or even like an outside observer of their own thoughts and feelings.

- Feeling disconnected from others. This can include not wanting to spend time with friends, family, or peers. Children and adolescents with PTSD may think that they don't fit anywhere and might have trouble connecting with other people.
- Hyperarousal symptoms are a final set that can occur in children and adolescents who develop PTSD. These symptoms may include:
- Difficulty sleeping, including more trouble falling asleep, staying asleep or waking up often during the night. Children and adolescents also may have nightmares about the traumatic event.
- Feeling nervous, anxious, or on edge. Their parents may describe children and adolescents as being clingy or dependent. This is because they are seeking reassurance from others that the traumatic event won't happen again.
- Frequently, feeling "keyed up" or on the edge of losing control. Children and adolescents who experience hyperarousal may have trouble maintaining their composure when they get angry or are provoked in certain situations. They may appear to be mean, sarcastic, aggressive or irritable to others around them and sometimes even to themselves.

These symptoms could occur immediately or be delayed for months or years following the trauma. Sometimes symptoms are very severe, and other times they are milder.

The following are some exercises you can do with your children to help them cope with this type of trauma:

1.) Tell a story and ask your child to retell what you just told them. Repeat, repeat and repeat. The more times they hear the story (this is true for all kids), the more likely they are to understand and remember. It helps them see your point of view by hearing the story from an outsider point of view. Try telling the story with a different voice any way that will help your child understand how you feel about the situation.

2. Tell a story about one of your own experiences similar to the experience your child is going through and retell what happened.

3. Draw pictures of something you think would be funny or strange and ask your child to draw with you.

4. Talk about the pictures they drew, just like they would talk about a video. They watched a movie together or something else fun that involved talking and sharing/observing things together.

5 . Have them watch an educational program with marketing messages. Tell them to help you select a program you think would be good for them. Watch it and talk about what they learn. The videos on Drs Foster and Smith are excellent for children because they teach how to be good citizens and deal with trauma.

6. Go out together and enjoy something fun together like a zoo, museum, or someplace fun together so you can observe the things your child is interested in or even new things.

7. Help your child make a bucket list of things they want to see & do before they grow up. The bucket list can be as big or small as

you would like. Have them share their lists with to prioritize what they want to see and do to make the most of your time together while trying to deal with trauma.

8. Develop a unique "trigger word" that means something positive for your child when it is time to go back into the trauma scenario (example: happiness, joy, love, beauty, respect, etc.).

9. Separate the trauma scenario into happy and sad parts (this can be very difficult for parents, so take turns imagining each piece as happy or sad.) The first time through the trauma scenario can be challenging, so try to keep your child safe and encourage him or her to tell you when they are okay.

10. Help them make up a list of things they like about themselves, making sure to include positive characteristics/skills they may not have realized were important to them.

11. Help them make up a list of things they like to eat/help them see that different people eat different types of food (not everyone eats the same way).

12. Help your child develop ways to be more active and help you keep track of how many steps they take each day. This will help them understand that even if you cannot walk, run, swim, or bike, it is still important to move every day.

13. Encourage them not to blame themselves for any part of the trauma and encourage them to focus on their recovery process.

14. Try different ways of eating food together like ice cream sundaes, ice cream cones, banana splits, smoothies, shakes.

Chapter 9
Complex Post-Traumatic Stress Disorder in Older Adults

M any people aged 65 and older have experienced a traumatic event, but not everyone who participates in a traumatic event will develop PTSD. If you are over 65 and you believe you may be experiencing symptoms of PTSD, there is help available. This chapter will provide information about what PTSD is, how to identify it in yourself or someone else, which treatments are effective for older adults with PTSD, and where to find help.

PTSD can result from any type of trauma such as war or terrorist attack, accident; natural disaster; violence; physical or sexual assault; kidnapping, or hostage situation. Research shows that a traumatic event does not need to be life-threatening to cause stress and anxiety. The symptoms for older people are similar for all other afflicted.

Trouble sleeping. A person with PTSD may have trouble going to sleep or staying asleep. They may wake up at night, have nightmares, or be agitated due to bad dreams. Some people with PTSD are also more likely to use alcohol and other drugs to fall asleep and stay asleep.

Trouble concentrating on tasks. A person with PTSD may have difficulty focusing on tasks, taking notes, or making decisions.

Acting out the trauma in some way. PTSD survivors may express their emotions through violence, alcohol or drug abuse, promiscuity, and gambling.

Feeling as though a traumatic event has ruined one's life. Some people feel as though they are never going to work again, enjoy a relationship again, or even have children again.

Becoming more defensive and suspicious toward others after a traumatic event that was not directed at them. A person with PTSD may feel that everyone is criticizing him or her and may even feel trapped.

Physically shaking, feeling edgy or agitated. Some people with PTSD experience extreme fear and anxiety in response to loud noise or smell. They may also experience rapid heart rate and sweating. They may also become easily frightened by other people's behavior, which scares them even further.

Increased irritability or anger toward others due to the trauma. It can be difficult for a person with PTSD to relax and engage in ordinary social interaction because they are so afraid of triggering flashbacks of the event.

Drug or alcohol abuse to calm down, forget the event, or escape from reality.

Having flashbacks, nightmares, and intense "movies in the head" about the traumatic event. Flashbacks are frightening images or thoughts about what happened during the traumatic event that suddenly seems real even when you are not experiencing them. Nightmares occur when you are sleeping and have all of the same symptoms as a flashback but happen when you are asleep.

Intrusive thoughts are unwanted memories, images, or ideas that can make it difficult to concentrate on anything else going on around you.

Feeling unusually or overly emotional such as feeling sad or hopeless, becoming more isolated, and having difficulty interacting with other people due to fear and anxiety. The feelings may be so intense that the sufferer wishes they were dead.

Difficulty with relationships based on feelings of distrust or being easily hurt. A person with PTSD may have trouble with family members, spouses, friends, and coworkers because they do not know how to behave in a trusting manner any longer.

Having trouble remembering important details of the traumatic event that is causing PTSD symptoms. A person who experienced trauma may have difficulty remembering what happened or even where they were during the event.

Behavioral changes including avoiding anything associated with the trauma event and withdrawing from other people. A person with PTSD may also have trouble being around other people after experiencing trauma because they are so afraid of having a flashback or thinking that something terrible will happen again.

Having trouble functioning in everyday life that interferes with work, school, relationships, and social activities. A person with PTSD may get sick more often, drive too fast, become accident-prone, have difficulty concentrating at work, lose their job, or drop out of a group.

Loss of interest in activities that used to bring pleasure, such as hobbies, sports, or even sex. A person with PTSD may feel too numb to enjoy anything anymore.

Having trouble coping with everyday daily life and activities such as work, school, friendships, or family. When a person with PTSD has a flashback or other intrusive thought, they may become overwhelmed and unable to sleep or function normally.

Feeling worthless and depressed. A person who experienced trauma may feel guilty for causing harm to themselves, others, or the world around them somehow. They may feel as though they are not good enough due to the trauma, that they can never go back to being the person they were before, and that no one will love them again.

Many people are not ready to learn about PTSD. This group includes friends and family members who have never experienced trauma. They may be afraid that they will get weak, start to feel bad or just plain not be able to handle the situation. A person with PTSD may try to protect a loved one from the experience of trauma by not sharing their concerns about it with them.

A person with PTSD is at increased risk for other conditions such as anxiety, depression, substance abuse, attention deficit-hyperactivity disorder (ADHD), bipolar disorder, and Alzheimer's disease due to the disruption in brain function long-term exposure to traumatic events. About 30% of people with PTSD will have suicidal thoughts at some point in their lifetime.

PTSD Awareness for the Public:

While it is essential to be aware that these symptoms of post-traumatic stress disorder (PTSD) exist, it is necessary not to treat a person with PTSD as fragile and weak. Everyone who experiences trauma goes through the same things that people with PTSD go through, and it may help if you can understand why they are behaving in specific ways. People who have experienced trauma need love, support, and compassion, not fear or criticism. With the proper permission from friends and family members, a person with PTSD can move forward in their life towards healing.

They can learn to understand the symptoms and how they are affecting them. They can learn strategies for dealing with trauma and work on any triggers they may have. Trauma is a part of life as it is a part of the human experience. What matters most is what happens after each person experiences it, how they choose to move forward in their life with or without treatment.

Awareness for Mental Health Professionals:

Trauma affects each person differently, and triggers vary significantly from person to person. Professionals who work with people must cope with trauma be as familiar with the new research on post-traumatic stress disorder as they are with the symptoms and signs of PTSD. They need to understand how the two illnesses are different while appreciating that they share many crucial behavioral components. The professional needs to be aware of their role in trauma treatment and know-how to ask a person how they are sensitive to their particular needs and concerns.

Chapter 10
Learning More about Complex PTSD

C omplex PTSD is a disorder that is characterized by a long-term pattern of exposure to traumatic events. A diagnosis may be given when an individual presents with symptoms from PTSD and the borderline personality disorder (BPD) criteria sets. Complex PTSD, like other kinds of trauma, can cause difficulties regulating emotions. Individuals with complex PTSD often experience a more severe form of PTSD and may also be more likely to have BPD. The patient may present with symptoms in interpersonal relationships, self-image, sexual identity, social identity, and interpersonal relations. Research has shown that these individuals are often in contact with the world around them and have a higher risk of abuse, neglect, and suicidal thoughts.

It's estimated that about 50% of those exposed to a traumatizing event will experience some symptoms at the time or in the following weeks, months, or even years. These symptoms match the diagnostic criteria for Post-Traumatic Stress Disorder (PTSD). In some cases, symptoms persist and may worsen over time. This is called chronic PTSD. Complex PTSD is a type of chronic PTSD with additional features not seen in other kinds of chronic PTSD, such as high dissociation and self-injury behaviors like cutting and burning skin.

We also know that many people have experienced trauma live happy lives without severe effects on their daily lives. So it boils down to this...what determines whether a person can go on living a happy life with PTSD and its symptoms? These are essential questions because many people have been successfully treated for their PTSD.

In most cases, family members are concerned about this behavior and spend a lot of time worrying about suicide attempts at home and even school. Frequently, these behaviors go unnoticed by friends and family who don't understand why someone would hurt him or herself in the first place. Treatment means telling loved ones what's going on...and with so many people being diagnosed with PTSD, do you want to go first?

These are the types of responses we typically see in individuals with Complex PTSD. Does this sound like a myth or an urban legend? It's not! There is considerable evidence to suggest that Complex PTSD may be more prevalent than previously thought. The most recent and up-to-date research shows great promise in understanding who suffers from Complex PTSD.

Complex PTSD occurs when the memories of an overwhelming experience in one's life become so powerful they cause a cascade of dysregulation (similar to PTSD symptoms) that affects many areas of functioning.

People with Complex PTSD have long-term effects that put them at risk for depression, anxiety, attention and concentration problems, and even alcohol and drug abuse. People without Complex

PTSD who live with trauma have higher rates of these same problems.

Research suggests that this type of trauma is more common than previously thought, with some estimates as high as 50% in children. Complex PTSD is a type of chronic PTSD that has features of both PTSD and dissociation. Dissociation is a psychological defense you can use to help protect yourself from overwhelming experiences and memories. The psychological reasons that result from Complex PTSD include:

These behaviors are manifestations of memories and information processing skills that are out of sync with reality. The information processing difficulties in people with Complex PTSD may include having internal modeling (relating to the present, as opposed to memory) problems, often resulting in poor judgments about their fears or thoughts about danger.

A hallmark of Complex PTSD is the relationship between information processing and reality processing. You are a member of a small group at work with five other people. One person in your group has left the office to go to lunch, leaving you all alone for 20 minutes. The rest of the group is at lunch, but they are having a great time without you there - you sit alone and don't enjoy the experience at all. You (the solitary person) need to join them because you want their company - but your loneliness makes it hard for you to do so. In other words, you are trying to get out of the situation but in such a way that you can avoid being alone.

Some people who have Complex PTSD may manage these fears or thoughts on a day-to-day basis, but most people with Complex PTSD can't. Very often, the thoughts and memories of these experiences become so overwhelming that it feels as if they are happening again - every day. People with Complex PTSD live in constant fear of reliving their trauma - like reliving the incident all over again each time they get ready for work or go to bed at night. The symptoms of Complex PTSD vary widely. Most people with Complex PTSD have persistent and intrusive memories from their traumatic events that they experience as flashbacks in which they are reminded of the original trauma. These memories can be activated by being reminded of the experience, such as hearing about a car accident or watching a news story about terrorism. These memories cause overwhelming anxiety and even seem to bring back the original overwhelming event for these individuals. The tricky part is that symptoms are not restricted to the initial trauma; thoughts and feelings about other past events may also become intrusive and cause anxiety or depression symptoms.

Complex trauma can have these characteristics including tendencies toward dissociation or splitting off memories or thoughts from other life experiences. People with complex trauma feel as if they are reliving the traumatic experience repeatedly in repetitive cycles of thinking, feeling, remembering, and responding to the event in various ways. This may be a person's primary coping response to trauma.

People with complex trauma feel as if they are reliving the traumatic experience repeatedly in repetitive cycles of thinking, feeling, remembering, and responding to the event in various ways. This may be a person's primary coping response to trauma. They suffer from persistent symptoms that don't go away. The person with complex trauma suffers from PTSD-like symptoms that do not diminish with time or with safe havens (such as therapy). These symptoms can include anxiety attacks, depression, suicidal thoughts and behavior, self-destructive behaviors, self-mutilation or self-injurious thoughts or behaviors, and intense anger toward others.

The person with complex trauma suffers from PTSD-like symptoms that do not diminish with time or with safe havens (such as therapy). These symptoms can include anxiety attacks, depression, suicidal thoughts and behavior, self-destructive behaviors, self-mutilation or self-injurious thoughts or behaviors, and intense anger toward others. They feel they are not safe in the world. The people who have Complex PTSD feel as if their world is unsafe, and they will be re-victimized at some point in their lives. This can cause feelings of being overly cautious about their surroundings.

Individuals who fall under the diagnosis of complex PTSD or BPD may not necessarily experience emotional difficulties due to their trauma. Instead, they experience problems between posttraumatic stress disorder (PTSD) symptoms that arise from traumatic events and other issues stemming from time spent seeing professionals for treatment purposes. In complex PTSD, BPD symptoms are not unique to the individual so much as they are connected to other sources of mental health issues such as dissociative disorder, depression, and substance use.

The pathophysiology behind complex PTSD is still not fully understood, and research is ongoing. Many theories can be proposed, such as a bi-directional relationship between trauma and PTSD or a connection between both disorders on a spectrum. Some studies have suggested a traitor genetic predisposition for complex PTSD, but most research has proved inconclusive.

What causes PTSD?

Scientists are not sure exactly what causes PTSD. However, many researchers believe that a series of biological and environmental factors play a role in developing PTSD. Genes that can be passed down from family members are one potential cause of developing PTSD. Research has found that children and adolescents who develop the disorder often have one or more close relatives with PTSD or other anxiety disorders. Similarly, chemicals in the brain, which help transmit signals between nerve cells, may also play a role in developing this disorder. These chemicals are called neurotransmitters, and two neurotransmitters in particular — serotonin and norepinephrine — seem to be linked to many anxiety disorders.

The environment also plays a role. While it's not always clear what causes PTSD in an individual, specific domains have been linked to developing it. For instance, individuals who are victims of rape or severe physical abuse are much more likely to develop PTSD than one might expect. Studies have shown that these types of experiences can affect people for a long time after they happen and make them more susceptible to developing the disorder.

The events may be so extreme that even years after the event occurs, the victim continues to relive the trauma through flashbacks.

Another cause is genetic. One in 20 American males is at risk of developing the disorder due to variations in the COMT gene that may cause greater exposure to stress hormones and various other factors.

People with PTSD may show signs of depression and anxiety, but that doesn't necessarily mean that they have PTSD. Depression, anxiety, insomnia, and other mental health conditions share symptoms with PTSD, so people who don't have it can still be treated effectively for their symptoms.

Psychotherapies target the root causes of combat-related PTSD by helping people understand what happened to them and how their current life situation has been affected by their traumatic experience.

In acute PTSD, the person's reactions are at their peak. This can lead to suicidal ideation (thoughts) or behaviors. These feelings of hopelessness and despair mustn't be ignored. With effective therapy or self-help methods, the person can overcome these feelings of sadness by talking about what happened, learning new coping skills, and finding ways to bring clarity and meaning to their experiences.

A combination of psychotherapy and medications can help with the symptoms of PTSD. Some common medicines used to treat PTSD include antidepressants such as selective serotonin reuptake inhibitors (SSRIs), such as citalopram (Celexa) or escitalopram (Lexapro), which may be used alone or in conjunction with a type of psychotherapy called cognitive-behavioral therapy. Another medication used to treat PTSD is clomipramine.

Psychotherapy alone is often recommended for people who have mild symptoms of PTSD because it allows the person to recognize their feelings without the intensity that comes with signs. Psychotherapy involves talking therapy, which may include supportive counseling or cognitive-behavioral therapy (CBT). It also involves individuals helping themselves overcome the effects of their trauma by facing those emotions and re-appraising their situations.

Psychotherapy

In severe cases, psychotherapy can lead to improvement in PTSD symptoms. However, psychotherapy can sometimes take a long time to work and can be hindered by cultural concerns about being seen as weak or coping with trauma. These can help people who've experienced trauma learn how to tolerate distress-related memories and learn new coping methods.

There may be many factors that play a role in developing PTSD, so it can be complicated. For this reason, learning how to treat your symptoms best can take some trial and error. Psychotherapy can sometimes take a long time to work and maybe hindered by cultural concerns about being seen as weak or able to cope with trauma. Therapy involves talking with a trained professional who helps you learn ways you can manage on your own. These therapies stress that the symptoms are not the person but the result of a traumatic experience. Therapy can also help people with PTSD understand the effects that their trauma has on them. Dealing with these feelings in therapy often helps lower anxiety and lessen the number of flashbacks and nightmares.

Cognitive-behavioral therapy (CBT) is one type of psychotherapy used to treat PTSD, as it helps people identify and change negative thought patterns and behaviors. CBT is a structured, goal-oriented therapy that teaches you to develop new ways of thinking about your trauma experiences. This can help you better cope with painful memories. You're encouraged to develop new ways of coping with these memories. This might include looking at negative or frightening thoughts and feelings in a new way or having new ways of reframing (changing how you think and feel about) your trauma experiences. You might be asked to identify triggers for your symptoms so that you learn how to control them. Several different types of CT have been developed since it was first introduced in the 1980s. In general, CT is often used for chronic PTSD patients who have too many symptoms to treat other therapies effectively. CT therapists focus on helping their patients reduce their anxiety and step out into every day, whole lives.

The main thing that distinguishes CT from other therapies is its focus on fear reduction instead of working through the trauma that causes the PTSD symptoms. Generally, exposure-based therapy is used as a form of treatment for people with complex PTSD. Trauma patients are exposed to their worst fears until they can achieve mastery over them. The relief of facing these memories allows patients to begin finding relief from their PTSD symptoms. The aim is for patients to unlearn their fear responses and return to normal.

In addition to working through traumatic memories, cognitive therapy (CT) can help patients learn to overcome their avoidance and detachment from the world and life in general. CT often focuses on helping the patient recognize signs of their trauma and develop insight into the cause of their symptoms. CT therapists concentrate on ways to avoid thinking about their traumatic memories but do not necessarily need to work with them directly through exposure. This helps with not feeling like a "lonely outsider," which can exacerbate mental illness.

Cognitive behavioral therapy (CBT) helps people to overcome the symptoms of complex PTSD by focusing on improving the way they deal with life situations. Assisting patients to achieve this in recognizing that even though they may suffer from traumatic memories, life does not have to be one continuous nightmare. CBT also focuses on teaching patients about their thoughts and behaviors and how these feelings can be changed. It is beneficial for patients who are not entirely convinced that their symptoms are caused by past trauma because it shows them how common these symptoms are, no matter what their cause may be.

Psychodynamic therapy (PT) focuses on helping patients with complex PTSD understand how their emotions affect how they perceive and react to the world. PT primarily focuses on assisting patients in coming to terms with their guilty feelings, which causes many people to avoid over-facing their fears. PT helps patients overcome this desire for escape by letting them live in a safe space where their emotions can be expressed. Some therapists believe that this will help them realize that the time to confront their fears has passed, while others say that this will help them feel more confident about facing their fears.

Many people with complex PTSD also suffer from comorbid substance abuse or other mental disorders. For those that struggle with substance abuse, drug treatment programs and behavioral therapy have proven effective in ending their drug use. Substance abuse can often make symptoms of PTSD worse, so patients need to enter a program that focuses on getting them clean and sober to improve their overall health.

While there is no cure for complex PTSD, treatments do appear to have positive results when used in conjunction with each other.

Regaining control of one's life is the ultimate goal of living with complex PTSD. So far, there has been success with using psychotherapy as one method to help patients fight their way back from this debilitating mental illness.

Additional information

One misunderstood concept is the disruption of the development of children, particularly regarding attachment. While it is accurate that a child who has experienced trauma may not form close attachments to others, this does not mean that the attachment system does not develop. The individual develops a new way of thinking in which self-regulation mechanisms are compromised due to repeated traumatic experiences. The individual will have what is referred to as an "attachment network" (a team of resources) to rely on support, but the client's traumatic experiences may heavily influence this network. This can give rise to symptoms of Complex PTSD.

Another misconception is that complex PTSD is only a disorder that affects women. The unique way women internalize traumatic events and their tendency toward coping with the resulting emotions through dissociation plays a part in developing complex PTSD.

Women may also be more likely to engage in dissociative tendencies. There may be some degree of biological predisposition for complex PTSD stemming from gender differences in how the brain develops.

BPD symptoms will vary concerning the individual, but some general symptoms include unstable relationships, trouble regulating emotions, fear of abandonment, extreme emotional reactions, impulsiveness, and self-harm tendencies. The development of BPD is influenced by how much the individual was subjected to traumatic events or how severely the trauma affected them.

Traumatic events can include various situations such as war, rape, natural disasters, or abandonment. Some circumstances could be complicated to overcome because they may involve other individuals who should be held responsible for what they are doing in child abuse. The main issue is that the victim and the perpetrator are often acquainted.

If an adult abuses or neglects a child, then the parent or guardian can be held legally liable. In domestic violence situations where there is more than one level of family involvement, there may also be a lack of clear blame, which may cause additional confusion for child victims and make it harder for them to understand what exactly has happened to them. In childhood sexual abuse, the predator may be close to the family, such as a relative or religious adviser.

The individual may have difficulty with interpersonal relationships due to their reliance on self-regulation mechanisms that are broken due to trauma. The person may have trouble knowing what they want from a relationship and how to maintain one. They also might feel that they are undeserving of pleasure or intimacy. This fits directly into the BPD criteria set. These individuals often suffer extreme emotional reactions when others quickly abandon close interpersonal relationships and can without warning.

Self-esteem is also an issue for these individuals. They may be able to understand themselves well but feel emotionally disconnected from the rest of the world. They experience a great deal of shame and guilt that can lead to self-harm, substance abuse, or other unhealthy practices, which are attempts to cope with feelings and emotions they cannot control.

Sexuality is another area that can be affected by complex PTSD. It has been successfully treated with the acceptance model of treatment, which involves slowly retraining behaviors and helping individuals gain confidence in their ability to have healthy sexual relationships to feel safe and secure.

Chapter 11
Case Study - Peter, a Young Soldier Who Lost His Life in the Gulf War

"This case study is about a young soldier named Peter, who had lost his life in the Gulf War. His battalion was stationed at some distance from where the fighting was going on. He volunteered for this mission because he wanted to prove himself as a man to his friends and family."

Peter's platoon was traveling westwards across Iraq. An Iraqi soldier stopped them with orders to destroy them and their vehicle with a rocket-propelled grenade launcher. The ambush came out of nowhere, and there seemed to be no way out that wasn't suicidal. Peter and the other soldiers jumped out of the moving vehicle while still in motion, chased by the Iraqi soldier and his weapon. The rest of Peter's platoon tried to help him, but none could get to him before he was hit in the chest by an RPG.

Peter lay on the ground, covered in blood and looking at his comrades running away from the ambush site. He didn't think that his life was over, but it didn't look good for him. The platoon leader gave orders to get Peter into a vehicle and take him safely where they could care for his wounds. The other men were confused and stunned at what had just happened. While they all waited for orders on what to do next, Peter lay there in the dirt, his heart pounding in his ears, his breaths coming in short pants.

The platoon leader ordered the soldiers to carry their fallen comrade to the vehicle parked nearby. The men stood around him as they took him towards their car, trying not to make too much noise. They moved very fast because if any Iraqis saw them or heard them, they would indeed be killed or captured themselves. The men placed Peter, who was barely conscious, in the back of the vehicle. They were all crying and whispering amongst themselves. They had no idea what to do - they were utterly dependent on their platoon leader for orders, which would be anything but easy to come by in this situation.

Peter lay there in the back of the vehicle as it started moving again towards safety. The soldiers cried as they sat in their seats beside him, tears coming down their faces and soaking his uniform with their salty tears. After a short time, he drifted off into a coma and died shortly after that.

The men had to cope with Peter's death for several days after. They all went into a state of shock, not knowing if they would make it home or be killed themselves. The mood in the whole battalion was pretty much the same as that of Peter's platoon, just waiting for orders and hoping they'd make it out alive.

The platoon leader felt a lot of grief and guilt over what happened. The platoon leader didn't have time to think about what happened that day, and he was just trying to keep his men alive and get them out of the situation they were in.

Peter's mother and father had a hard time coping with his death. They felt a whole range of emotions after receiving the news that their son had been killed in action. His mother was most concerned that she lost her son so young and before they could share their lives. She wanted him back more than anything else in the world but knew nothing she could do.

Peter's wife didn't take his death as hard as his parents did. She was concentrating on her new baby and the fact that she would have to do many things for the two children. She also felt guilty about the fact that she had no time with Peter while he was alive, so she vowed to spend as much time as possible with him now that he was gone.

The platoon leader, his fellow soldiers and their families all suffered from the loss of a young man just like Peter. They mourned his passing and honored him as a soldier who gave his life trying to save others in battle.

It's important to understand what PTSD is and how it can affect those who suffer from it. When someone suffers a traumatic event, like Peter experienced, their brain has difficulty processing the experience in a healthy way. Their mind may play tricks on them by making them feel as if the event is happening again or bringing back memories of the event they want to forget.

There are other ways PTSD can affect people too. They may become anxious or aggressive easily. This is because the learning center of the brain, called the amygdala, is locked into conflict with other areas of the brain that are trying to overcome the trauma. The amygdala is responsible for how much we pay attention to what we're doing and how much emotion we express.

Peter's story begins with three actions that triggered his PTSD: PTSD is not something everyone has to worry about. Only a small percentage of those who suffer from it begin having symptoms as Peter did: physical reactions like having trouble sleeping or have trouble concentrating at work.

The physical reactions that Peter experienced were not uncommon among those who suffer from PTSD. Peter's first flashback occurred while he was sleeping. It was an effect of having viewed footage from his tour in Iraq just before going to bed. From there he began to avoid watching any media news related to terrorism for fear that he might have as a flashback about it; He believed the brain would link two separate events together through similar sensory triggers. Peter also had trouble sleeping and would wake up at odd hours of the night. At first, his wife tried to help him with his sleep issues, but after a while, he began avoiding her and even felt angry about her attempts to help him. This caused the couple to become estranged and eventually divorce.

After having separated from his wife, Peter developed a fear of abandonment, causing him to isolate himself. He began calling himself "the guy who needs company" and avoided going out and socializing because he was afraid that people would laugh at or talk bad about him for his experiences in Iraq. He also started drinking alcohol in order to reduce the emotional effects of PTSD on him.

After his breakup with his wife, the nightmares began. Peter had been sleeping with a pillow under his head because that was the only way he could get some rest. When he began to have nightmares from experiencing flashbacks as a result of watching material related to the war, he felt safer putting something under the pillow so that he could still get rest. However, that did not work out in this case because his nightmares were not related to watching anything about the war. His dreams were about being back in Iraq and that everyone he knew had been killed in a battle (not seeing them again). He also experienced physical reactions such as nausea and sweating when having these dreams.

Peter's physical reactions to his nightmares caused him to begin drinking even more which led him to develop a dependency. In order to stop the nightmares, he needed to calm down. This was when his addiction started. After Peter started drinking, however, he began experiencing even more problems in his life: He had lost some of his ability to concentrate and became angry and irritable. As a result of this, Peter quit working at his job as a taxi driver, which led him into financial trouble. The VA helped pay for some of the expenses that PTSD has caused him and is helping with therapy for recovery.

According to Dr. Frank Ochberg, who developed the diagnosis of PTSD in 1980, Peter has a mild case of PTSD. He believes that for people to develop PTSD, they need to have a couple things happen. First, they need to have a traumatic event happen to them. In this case it was Peter's tour at war in Iraq; Second, they need to keep having flashbacks about the war or some other event that happened while at war; Third, they become avoidant and avoid others because they are afraid that people will laugh at them for their experiences at war.

According to Dr. John Briere, who also developed the diagnosis of PTSD in 1980, most cases of PTSD are seen in soldiers who have been involved in battle or have seen a lot of combat during the war. Peter took part in war and fought men who he knew had been killed. Those soldiers may have left their families and communities to fight for their country. This means that they may come back with a greater sense of loss than other veterans because they are not only fighting for their own lives but also fighting against what it really is like to lose another human being; since there were no winners when two sides are fighting they battle. And when they come back, they do not want to be the ones that are left behind.

Also, with the veterans who have a tougher time dealing with their reactions to PTSD are those who were wounded in battle or whose loved ones were wounded. Peter's wife was killed so he shared similar experiences to those who have lost their loved ones. Also, while many soldiers are in a combat zone for only one tour of duty, Peter was there for four years and this can make it harder for him to return to what was his life before he went.

PTSD has been associated with suicidal thoughts and behaviors. For example, a study of 7,000 veterans who originally screened negative for PTSD found that those who screened positive for PTSD at the time of their discharge were twice as likely to be diagnosed with PTSD during the following twelve months. A longitudinal analysis found that soldiers who had suicidal thoughts prior to deployment or combat experience in the past were more likely to engage in suicidal behaviour post-deployment.

Note: Among Vietnam Veterans, those with PTSD are 2–4 times more likely to commit suicide than other veterans; however those with only a history of major depression are no more likely to commit suicide than non-veterans without depression. A longitudinal study of 6,907 veteran suicide attempts or deaths revealed that repeated suicide-related outcomes were more likely among veterans who had PTSD (27.5%) than those without PTSD (19.6%). Most suicides within the sample were preceded by a depressive disorder and 87% of suicides were preceded by a substance abuse disorder.

Chapter 12
Coping with Someone Suffering from PTSD

I f I had a dollar for every time someone told me they have PTSD or that their friend has PTSD, I'd be a wealthy woman. Although the cause of this disorder is not completely understood by experts and doctors, it's likely to stem from an event in your life which really shook you up. Whether it was wartime combat, assault or rape, it can be difficult to adjust back to regular life afterwards.

They sometimes experience flashbacks of whatever traumatized them (either vividly recalling these memories or dreaming about them), avoidance behaviors (such as staying away from social events), negative changes in thoughts and feelings (such as feeling unsafe) and destructive changes in behaviors (such as using drugs).

Self-help

1) Try not to isolate yourself. It's natural to want time alone after an event that shook you up, but compound this by staying away from friends and family and people who care about you, and it can become extremely isolating. Eventually, socializing again will become easier after time passes—but in the meantime, don't be afraid to reach out for help from your loved ones.

2) Be truthful to yourself. If you're struggling with trust issues, it can be easy to lie to yourself about how you've been feeling. Everyone has a different threshold, but if you're not talking about what happened in great detail with a trusted friend or therapist, you may delay the healing process.

3) Try to avoid seeing others who have PTSD. This is easier said than done—but being around someone who has this disorder can make you feel worse. Try to limit your social interactions, and try not to be around those who would trigger bad memories for you.

4) Remind yourself that everyone has their own challenges right now; they aren't coping differently just because PTSD is part of their life. If you take a moment to understand what someone with this disorder is going through, the recovery process may seem less scary.

5) Don't blame yourself for what happened. It's easy to think, "If I hadn't been there, this wouldn't have happened." Instead of blaming yourself, realize that you didn't cause what happened; you're just dealing with the repercussions afterwards.

6) Practice self-care. If possible, start small—for example, making a quick trip to the grocery store can help you feel more grounded in your own life.

7) Try not to take on too many responsibilities. Before you know it, everything else in your life may seem overwhelming and stressful.

8) Try writing down your thoughts and feelings about the situation which traumatized you. Many people experience relief from

writing what's on their mind; it can be therapeutic for you to write about what happened, how it made you feel and what came after.

9) Remember that most people are good. If you've been exposed to trauma and violence, it's hard to accept the fact that most people are inherently compassionate and kind. But try telling yourself that most people will treat you with respect, and perhaps your PTSD symptoms can start to feel more manageable.

10) Take notes on what makes you feel better. When you're feeling down or anxious, try different techniques—listening to soft music, seeing a friend, going for a walk, meditating—and see which ones help you feel better after an episode of anxiety or fear.

11) Don't beat yourself up. Try not to focus on how you feel and where you aren't coping at the moment. This can lead to frustration, resentment and feelings of being hopeless. We're all human beings—it's okay to accept your situation as it is, and then work towards a change that will make you happy again.

12) Try quitting any substance abuse or use in moderation if you are addicted; this may be difficult if your life is already in turmoil. But knowing that there will be good days and bad ones (and that eventually the bad days will end) does help people tend to progress into recovery more quickly. This article has more information.

13) Believe in yourself. PTSD causes a lot of anxiety, so it's no surprise that you may feel down on yourself during recovery. When you're having a bad day, give yourself credit for trying your best

to cope with what's going on in your life. None of us is perfect—so don't expect to be able to cope perfectly either!

14) Try not to use alcohol and drugs as a coping mechanism for stress or feelings of sadness. While drugs and alcohol may help you in the short run, they are a slippery slope that can lead you to more trouble down the line. If you're using to numb yourself, realize that it's not making your PTSD symptoms any easier—it's just keeping you from addressing them.

15) Try to learn how to be assertive and ask for what you need. It's easy to become passive in your interactions with others when you're dealing with PTSD. But again, asking for what you need will help you feel happier and less overwhelmed.

16) Keep your life as normal as possible. It's easy to isolate yourself when you deal with PTSD, but this will only make the situation worse in the long run. Try scheduling "normal" events like lunch with a friend or spending time with family members who are understanding and supportive. The more time you spend around other people, the more your mind can accept that things are normal and that there is a brighter future ahead of you.

17) Try not to expect too much of yourself. Most people who experience trauma and PTSD aren't able to go back to what they were doing before the trauma occurred. This can be frustrating, but it's important not to get angry or resentful towards yourself for not functioning normally right now.

18) Don't focus on what you can't do; focus on what you can do instead. When you're feeling overwhelmed, it's easy to think

about all the things you used to enjoy that are now impossible due to your symptoms of PTSD.

19) Remember that you are not alone—about 6.8 million people in the United States experience PTSD during any given year, and recovery is possible! You don't have to feel ashamed for not managing well right now; we all need some extra support now and then.

20) Create a list of strategies you can use when you're feeling bad. It's easier to be aware of things that work for you when you have them written down in an easy-to-access place.

How to spot PTSD

Well-documented cases of PTSD have been found among Holocaust survivors and victims of violent crime, sexual abuse, car accidents, train wrecks and airplane crashes. It doesn't matter how an event occurs or what kind it is — the crucial factor is how much stress you experience from it. According to PTSD expert and psychologist, Dr. James Baraniuk, the main features of this disorder include:

The person usually feels intense fear, helplessness and guilt. He may also have nightmares about the event and feel emotionally numb. While the symptoms of PTSD usually begin within days of the traumatic experience, they can persist for months or even years afterwards. PTSD is associated with depression and anxiety as well as substance abuse problems in some people.

The cause of PTSD is not fully understood, but experts think that the brain's fear center is temporarily affected. The symptoms of PTSD are usually mild to moderate in the early stage. You or a loved one may also have disturbing thoughts and feelings of guilt or shame about the traumatic event.

In later stages, however, your symptoms tend to be more severe. These include flashbacks (revisiting the traumatic experience), nightmares and emotional numbness (lack of interest in things that were formerly pleasurable). If you experience severe PTSD during these later stages, you might also have chronic physical problems such as difficulty sleeping or feeling agitated or jumpy. You may even become socially isolated and avoid situations or conversations that remind you of the traumatic experience.

In some people, PTSD symptoms can last for years. The condition is usually treated with medication and psychotherapy. But treatment is most successful when it's begun right after the traumatic event occurs. If you've ever experienced a traumatic event, chances are you've also experienced post-traumatic stress disorder (PTSD). More than just a mental health problem, PTSD goes beyond the feeling of anxiety that many people associate with it. To better understand what the disorder entails and how to cope with it, read on for a brief overview and list of resources.

Post-traumatic stress disorder is an anxiety condition that can happen to anyone who has gone through some sort of trauma. It's not just reserved for veterans or soldiers; anyone can develop PTSD after experiencing an intense event or events like natural disasters, car accidents, assaults, sexual abuse or other traumatic incidents. Symptoms include feelings of distress, sleep disturbances, flashbacks or nightmares, anger or irritability, and being easily startled.

People who've gone through trauma may experience PTSD symptoms for only a short time after the event. But for others, the symptoms can last months or years and can sometimes lead to other mental health conditions like depression. Fortunately, PTSD is treatable with therapy and a number of other treatment options.

If you've experienced a traumatic event in your life, you may have developed post-traumatic stress disorder (PTSD) or be at risk of developing it. It's a complicated condition that can affect your day-to-day life, and while there isn't one way to cope with PTSD, these tips can help guide the way.

Get Help

It is wise to learn more about how to cope by staying on top of PTSD symptoms like flashbacks and nightmares. Maintain healthy habits like getting enough sleep and eating properly. Find ways to stay active like exercising or joining a support group for survivors. Seek out professional help from a therapist who specializes in trauma recovery or advocacy groups for rape victims/survivors.

Talking about what happened is a key part of overcoming PTSD. Reach out to those who you feel safe around, such as close friends and family. Ask for support from them in the form of an ear to listen or someone to help you feel like you're not alone.

If you experience PTSD symptoms, get help right away. Let friends, family members and support groups know what you're going through so they can offer support and encourage you to seek treatment as soon as possible.

Chapter 13
More About PTSD

P TSD may result when people are exposed to one of two types of trauma, both in which they experience, witness, or learn about unexpected or violent death. Traumatic events cause people to develop PTSD including military combat, natural disasters, rape, torture, and child abuse. It is complex so let's take a final overview look.

What happens to you? You go about the day in a daze, and it's hard to concentrate. You're constantly startled for no reason. One minute you're crying and the next you're elated, or alternatively, going numb with shock and terror. These are all symptoms of post-traumatic stress disorder - PTSD - an anxiety disorder that affects many people around the world who have been through traumatic happenings such as violence, disaster or abuse. It can take years to develop symptoms of PTSD, but they won't just go away on their own if left untreated; you need to look into getting help before depression starts setting in too deeply.

PTSD is a major mental health problem. It's more likely than most people think it is, as the World Health Organization (WHO) estimates that one in 20 adults suffer from PTSD at some point in their life. Think about a brave and strong individual who has overcome tremendous amounts of pain and suffering to achieve such high levels of success. Many people believe this is the case. However, if you look at the psychological profiles of those who have left war zones or experienced a traumatic event, it's likely that you will often find multiple cases of PTSD before the person has returned home.

PTSD is not very well understood by most people - in fact, less than one percent of doctors and even fewer mental health professionals understand the intricacies of PTSD and its symptoms at all. It was only until relatively recently that studies were being conducted on those who had been through trauma to determine how they coped with their emotions.

No one knows exactly how PTSD is formed, but experts have determined that it is based on the theory that the human mind has four main psychological defense systems - the fight or flight system (when you're scared for your life, you respond by fighting, running from your attacker or fleeing in an attempt to escape), the protective system (when you're in a dangerous situation, this defense system will instinctively take over), the behavioral inhibition system (when you see something bad happening to someone close to you like a loved one or friend, this will also trigger behavioral inhibition) and finally, the attachment and bonding system (if a human being is threatened by an animal, he will tend to defend it as if it were his own child).

When one of these systems is activated, it causes the body to release certain chemicals such as adrenaline, cortisol and many others that cause the body to feel high levels of stress. These chemicals are released in order to prepare the body for fighting or fleeing. When the event is over, the natural thing for a human being to do is tend his wounds and try to recover from PTSD. The problem begins when there are no natural outlets for these chemicals to be released.

Some people who have been through traumatic events have been able to deal with their emotions effectively by using healthy outlets such as journaling or consulting with a therapist; this can help them recover from traumatic events much more quickly than those who continue down a dark path of self-destruction. In the case of others, however, there are no healthy outlets for their emotions and they may end up having undue stress and anxiety for much longer than they should.

In this case, a person will likely continue to have PTSD until he or she is able to find some way to release the chemicals that his body is producing. If this person doesn't heal properly from PTSD, he may resort to destructive behaviors in order to cope with the pain that he's feeling - for example, a man who was in war might turn to alcohol or drugs as a way to escape his memories and emotions. This can cause him to become an addict and bring a whole new set of problems along.

PTSD is most commonly experienced during a time when a person feels helpless, hopeless and powerless. If you've ever had PTSD symptoms during times of high stress, you'll know that it can make you feel as though your life is out of control.

When PTSD affects you in such a way as to cause depression, it will continue to take its toll upon your mind and emotional health for months or even years after the initial trauma has occurred.

Many people who do not seek help with their condition may end up having severe psychological problems before they even realize that something is wrong.

PTSD doesn't have to be a source of pain and suffering; it can also be a tool that helps people to become stronger and more resilient in the face of tragedy. It's important to know that PTSD is treatable, but only if the person receiving treatment has open communication with their doctor and allows them to help him or her.

PTSD is not the result of weakness and lack of character - it's a disease that requires the strength and courage to seek help.

Recap: Post-Traumatic Stress Disorder (PTSD) Symptoms:

Anxiety and fear: The most obvious form of PTSD occurs when someone has been exposed to a trauma or traumatic event. These symptoms are often triggered by flashbacks where the person will be shown a memory that reminds them of the trauma.

Sleep problems: People who have PTSD often report having trouble sleeping. This may be caused by the symptoms of depression due to the trauma or it's possible that the sleep those who suffer from PTSD were getting before the trauma was disrupted.

Insomnia: Many people with PTSD are not able to sleep for days or even weeks after a traumatic incident, so they will have trouble falling asleep as well. Sleep disturbances during this phase can cause memory issues and other cognitive difficulties.

Flashbacks: The most common symptoms of PTSD are flashbacks where the person will relive a moment of horror from their past event in their mind and body. These flashbacks can be triggered at random or at certain times in the person's life.

Nightmares: While some people who suffer from PTSD may have nightmares that they are being threatened by a dangerous person, others will have more severe nightmares where they relive the event in their own mind over and over again. These nightmares are often terrifying and leave the victim feeling like their losing control of their own mind.

PTSD is defined in different ways for different groups of people including veterans, those in the military, civilians, children who witness violence and then develop PTSD later in life; they also talk about how PTSD has been underdiagnosed or even misdiagnosed due to unique experiences with trauma. Understanding all the ramifications comes from looking at the role of PTSD in history. PTSD was first observed in World War I soldiers and that it gradually became more accepted as time went on. PTSD was first identified by a psychiatrist named Janet Travell who coined the word when she proposed that traumatized individuals reacted to their experiences with a psychological illness rather than insanity.

Nonetheless, the effects of traumatic events are often ignored or dismissed by the people involved, but that over time, both society and medicine began to pay more attention.

PTSD has evolved over time and is known to affect anybody regardless of age, gender, or race. PTSD has been broken down into three categories based on how it is seen in people; this includes exposure to trauma, re-experiencing symptoms, and avoidance symptoms.

It is now part of the DSM, the diagnostic manual created by American psychiatrist Robert Spitzer in 1994. The international version of the DSM, called the International Classification of Diseases (ICD), was created by a group of mental health specialists from across the world.

The psychological consequences of repeated exposure will continue to build up until they reach a point where they cannot be ignored. At this point, a host of unpleasant symptoms will emerge. These symptoms will not disappear overnight - but they can be reduced using professional treatment options which could help you cope with your condition better.

We all have stress in our lives. It's inevitable and there's no way to avoid it. But what happens when that stress spills over into your life outside of work? What happens when it impacts the relationships you have with those around you — your family, friends, spouse?

The National Institute of Mental Health (NIMH) reports that one in three adults in the United States, and as many as one in five soldiers returning from war, suffer from PTSD. According to NIMH, women are twice as likely as men to experience PTSD.

This statistic is especially surprising because women have traditionally had an easier time dealing with stress and trauma.

PTSD is not a condition that you just get over by not thinking about the trauma anymore. In fact, avoiding thinking about it can make your symptoms worse. It's a serious mental health condition that must be addressed with treatment by mental health professionals like psychologists or psychiatrists. The symptoms of PTSD can be mild, moderate, or severe, and can last for more than a month.

Some people with PTSD don't experience any symptoms at all. Others have only some of the symptoms listed below. A diagnosis of PTSD requires that a person have at least one symptom in each of the three categories: reliving the event (also called re-experiencing), avoiding reminders of it, and increased arousal (being on edge).

Sudden or unexpected shocks can trigger reactions in people who are suffering from PTSD — triggers that cause their feelings to come back to them as if they are still experiencing the trauma they went through. For example, if you've been sexually assaulted, a loud noise or a sudden movement can bring the memory back to you. You may feel upset or sad, and be afraid that someone is going to hurt you. Or you may experience an intrusive flashback in which horrible memories of the trauma are replaced with terrifying images.

To make matters worse, it can be difficult to stay calm. You may have trouble sleeping, or feel tired all the time. You may even realize, for the first time, that you actually do experience more physical symptoms from your trauma than you used to — like heart palpitations or stomach problems. Or some people find that they have difficulty concentrating on schoolwork or remembering things (called an attention deficit disorder).

People with PTSD usually start experiencing symptoms during a traumatic event that are mild but can grow progressively worse over time. In fact, if they don't get treatment, symptoms often go from mild to moderate. You may start having flashbacks at the same time you experience the event. Flashbacks are a vivid re-experiencing of the trauma that can make it seem like you're reliving it. Symptoms include:

Intrusive thoughts about the traumatic event (images, memories) that appear without warning and repeatedly disrupt your daily routine. A constant feeling that the traumatic event is happening again.

Feeling as though you are experiencing the traumatic event all over again (flashbacks, nightmares). Intense physical sensations which represent trauma on a visceral level. This means experiencing the trauma in your body and not just in your mind. For example, some people with PTSD feel overwhelming feelings of loss when they see someone or something that reminds them of the traumatic experience — like a favorite shirt that reminds them of their sexual assault — and they feel their heart breaking all over again. Others may actually see things crumbling around them, or have visions of losing control and going crazy.

Amnesia can occur when the brain tries to protect you from the pain of your memories. But if these gaps in memory cause problems, like forgetting important dates or conversations, then amnesia is a sign that you need some help. When it gets to this point, it is very important to seek treatment for PTSD because the avoidance of symptoms can be as damaging as experiencing them. This makes it hard for you to recover from the traumatic experience because it isolates you from people who could offer support.

Severe Symptoms

When someone with PTSD has been exposed to so much trauma that it alters their ability to function normally, the symptoms become severe. Severe symptoms are actually the same as moderate symptoms but they are more intense and can affect your life in more negative ways. Maybe you have trouble functioning at work or school, or you're experiencing severe depression, addiction to drugs or alcohol, insomnia or nightmares every night. These are all signs that you need help to recover from PTSD.

How Does PTSD Affect Your Sleep?

They'll also experience more nightmares, which can keep them awake. They may also be hyper-aroused, which means they have trouble calming down after a nightmare or other stressful event. In addition, a person with PTSD may associate certain places with the traumatic event that keeps them awake, like their bedroom if the trauma occurred in that room.

What you can do for better sleep: Avoiding your problems won't make them go away. You must first work through them if you want to feel better. If you're struggling with insomnia, or have sleep problems after your traumatic experience and you don't know what else to do, here are some steps you can take:

- Find a therapist who understands trauma and PTSD. Talk therapy is the recommended treatment for dealing with trauma-related symptoms.

- Make sure your doctor has been trained in cognitive-behavioral therapy (CBT) for PTSD and knows how to treat it so it doesn't get worse. These doctors know how to monitor the effects of a particular therapy over time, so they can prevent any setbacks that might occur in the healing process.

- Do things that require physical activity or other brain stimulation so you'll fall asleep faster at night.

- Other things you can do to help yourself sleep better: avoid caffeine and other stimulants for several hours before bed, try meditating, exercising or listening to relaxing music before bedtime, write down your thoughts or feelings in a journal, stay away from your phone and computer at least 30 minutes before bed, get eight hours a night instead of just six if possible, and keep a regular schedule that allows for 8-9 hours of sleep each night.

- Wear comfortable clothing to bed, like loose pants and t-shirt vs. fitted pajamas, don't check your phone or computer right before bed, and don't have a thermostat that keeps the house too warm.

- You can have better sleep at home: If you find yourself sleeping better in a hotel or hostel, try to do what you can to make it more like home. The following tips may help:

- Take your shoes off before you walk through the door. If you have to step on a creaky floorboard or squeaky stair step or two, just deal with it now. Save the potential for real damage for later when you're trying to sleep.

- Turn your phone and computer on airplane mode before bedtime, then put them away in another room so you won't be tempted to check them in the middle of the night.

- Create a reading environment: although it's perfectly fine to read on your phone, devices and screens often emit blue light which can disrupt the production of melatonin. The closer you are to the screen, the more likely you are to fall asleep with your phone in a place that's too bright. Turn your phone face down and keep it away from your bed at night. Make sure there are no bright lights in the bedroom at night.

If you want to feel sleepy even after reading in bed rather than falling right asleep, make sure to read right before bedtime.

Don't wait until you're falling asleep to start reading because you won't be able to stay awake. You may have to take a short break from reading in order to enjoy the book and fall asleep at the same time. If you're training yourself for a long period of time (like 30-60 minutes) then schedule your times for reading in bed until your body gets used to the routine and you can fall asleep more easily without having a book on hand. While you're doing this, make sure to read a book you enjoy, something you look forward to reading.

Myths and stereotypes about people with PTSD are confusing and damaging over time. Although PTSD is more common among veterans than the general population, it's certainly not exclusive to those who served in the armed forces — especially because it also affects people who have never been deployed or been in combat at all. For example, if you have a family member with PTSD, you may be wondering how they can have it after they didn't go through the traumatic event that caused them to develop symptoms.

The fact is that your family member may have had it months or years before, and while this may not always be the case, triggers like seeing a traumatic event or hearing someone else mention one are enough to cause symptoms to re-emerge.

Many people with PTSD are unaware of what is triggering their symptoms because often it is just small things that can set them off. It could be loud noises, or crowds of people, or being alone in a room that they associate with the trauma. For example, someone who was sexually assaulted may begin experiencing symptoms after locking themselves in their bathroom for the first time. Someone who was involved in a car accident may need to hold their breath while driving over a bridge.

These experiences may cause symptoms to appear for the first time, which is why it's important to seek help if you think you're suffering from PTSD or if you have experienced a traumatic event and are wondering if you should be seeking treatment for it.

Conclusion

D o you know what a mental disorder is? Mental disorders are illnesses that affect people's moods, thoughts and behavior. People with mental disorders may have difficulty coping with daily life and work.

The Diagnostic and Statistical Manual of Mental Disorders, Fifth Edition (DSM-5) is an organized list of diagnostic criteria that psychologists use to diagnose mental disorders in children, teenagers, adults, and the elderly. It includes specific diagnostic categories such as major depressive disorder or obsessive-compulsive disorder. DSM-5 also contains descriptions of symptoms for each diagnosis as well as possible treatments for them.

Complex post-traumatic stress disorder (C-PTSD) is a mental disorder that develops after experiencing an event or series of events that is so horrifying or overwhelming that it feels as if a person's life will never be the same again.

C-PTSD occurs in approximately 1 in 10 Americans who have been exposed to extremely traumatic events such as rape, warfare or torture. It has also been studied among those with complicated grief (not discussed here). C-PTSD is considered worse than PTSD because it is a combination of the feelings and symptoms of PTSD and other disorders. In addition, people who have it can't just be treated with medication alone like those with PTSD can.

The signs of complex post-traumatic stress disorder include physical problems such as chronic pain, gastrointestinal (GI) disorders and headaches. These are commonly seen in children who have lived through sexual abuse or other forms of trauma that caused them to feel helpless.

A rape victim may have nightmares or flashbacks of the rape. She may have trouble sleeping. She may abuse drugs or alcohol to deal with her feelings. She might not be able to feel any positive emotions (such as love) for her baby, and she might become increasingly difficult to live with because of this.

Complex post-trauma has been associated with other disorders such as depression, anxiety disorders, brain injury or epilepsy. These other disorders can be a source for the symptoms experienced by someone with C-PTSD. For example, someone with epilepsy who had an episode that was disrupted by flashing lights may have short term memory loss if they were rushed to an emergency room after the incident. They might also be more emotionally sensitive than others to these seizures and thus more likely to seek help when they occur. This means that they may then be diagnosed with C-PTSD.

Some people also report experiences of being "the other". After living with a parent who swore at them, hit them or abused them in some way, they may have felt that they were not worthy of being loved or lovable by others because of this. A person who has been abused as a child may reject further relationships because any partner will also be abusive and their loved ones will not be around for long. In this case, the trauma is compounded by a feeling of being the other and the lack of positive relationships with others.

Although C-PTSD was only first recognized in 1994, clinicians have long known that it exists. For example, children who had been in residential treatment and had suffered from abuse or neglect were more likely to develop symptoms of depression than those who did not have such experiences. Today, there are still many people who are not aware that C-PTSD exists and may never be diagnosed.

There are several reasons for this. First, those with C-PTSD often appear to have problems in functioning that overlap with many other conditions that also involve depression, anxiety or phobias. For example, people with C-PTSD may feel that they cannot live a normal life and these feelings take them to therapy. In this case, they are in treatment for anxiety or another disorder such as depression. People suffering from C-PTSD may also be suffering from other conditions, at the same time, which makes it harder to notice that the C-PTSD is separate from the other issues.

The fact that the symptoms of C-PTSD are similar to those of other disorders also means that some people with that condition do not have it. For example, if people with C-PTSD have been in therapy from an early age and have learned to use their feelings, they are less likely to be aware of their condition.

C-PTSD does not always result in PTSD. Some people with the condition do not develop anxiety or depression. Instead, they may experience a dissociative state or a dissociative identity disorder (DID). For example, a person could be abused by several different people at different times and feel that the trauma is being repeated over and over again. In this case, the person may be able to function in daily life and have no symptoms of PTSD. However, the trauma of the abuse is still being experienced as a single event. Some people who have C-PTSD may also experience dissociative episodes that do not fall within any label other than PTSD. For example, some people with C-PTSD have flashbacks or intrusive thoughts that take them back to their worst experiences. Some people may experience these feelings all the time and would not be able to talk about or share their experiences with others. Others may feel that these feelings are normal and part of everyday life in a way that is impossible for other people to understand.

People with C-PTSD can experience many different symptoms, but most often they experience nightmares and flashbacks. This may be a result of their inability to move on. These nightmares and flashbacks may also be a result of fearing that their current situation may become a repeat of the past or that they are going to lose control.

This fear causes them to feel vulnerable and threatened. C-PTSD people tend to have poor concentration, if they are even able to concentrate at all. They usually avoid thinking about past experiences because it causes them so much pain, which makes it hard for them to function in daily life as well as it would have before the PTSD diagnosis occurred. In this way, PTSD can create a vicious cycle in which the survivor has little time or energy to deal with their many other issues.

Survivors

Survivors of trauma often blame themselves for the traumatic event because they feel as if they can have somehow prevented it from happening. This feeling of guilt is not uncommon and is obviously a normal response to an abnormal situation. The person may feel that if they had been more aware or more careful, they could have prevented their trauma from occurring.

For example, a rape survivor may feel that she should have been able to stop her assault by using the self-defense techniques she learned. If she had remembered to close her locker door, the attack would not have happened.

Survivors may also be angry at themselves because they did not know what was happening, they are unable to remember what happened or they are unable to control their own bodies. Again this is something that anyone who has experienced trauma will feel. However, by blaming themselves or being angry at oneself for the experience is not helpful and can be destructive because it keeps people in emotional pain and prevents them from experiencing normal human joys and relationships again.

The most important thing for survivors to do is to recognize that they are not to blame. It is important to accept that they could not have prevented the event from taking place and that there is no way that they could have known what was happening. They may also need to recognize that they did the best they could at the time and these feelings are normal. As mentioned previously, people who have been abused as children often do not know how to deal with their feelings in a healthy way and may experience their emotions as overwhelming.

Many people with C-PTSD experience mood swings because of this. They may have a good day, which could even result in a breakthrough, and then fall into a deep mood of intense sadness. This sadness is more likely to be the result of living with memories of overwhelming trauma than being sad about something else and having no outlet for their emotions. However, it is important to remember that this is not depression or another mood disorder because C-PTSD does not involve the feelings of depression that people with these other disorders experience.

Survivors often feel shame and embarrassment about what happened to them. They might feel that they were at fault for having been abused in some way or they might feel as if they are dirty because their attacker touched them in a way that was inappropriate. When someone is raped, they feel as if they have lost control over their own body. In this case, the survivor may actually feel as if they are not human and that having been raped does not make any sense.

The survivor may also feel like a victim because they were powerless to prevent the attack from taking place. In this case, people who have been abused or assaulted may withdraw from others because they do not want to be reminded of what happened or they may become dependent on their support system. This is often a result of their feeling unsafe with others and their feeling that somebody else can protect them from harm in some way.

Surrounding oneself with others is a very important part of feeling safe. If the survivor does not have this safe situation, they often feel as if they are being watched at all times and that people are watching to see if they will relapse into their old ways. They may also feel like nobody can understand what happened to them or that everybody is too busy to notice how bad they feel.

This is an understandable phenomenon when one has been abused or assaulted because of course there are other people around who could care less about the victim's feelings and want them out of their sight as soon as possible, particularly in an emergency situation where the victim needs help immediately.

It is important to remember that the survivor is not being a bad person or making a mistake by doing this.

It is more likely the other way around because the survivor feels that they cannot feel safe unless they are alone and feel as if they can hide their most painful emotions from others. In time, they may learn to overcome this and come to understand that there are other people out there who will also be there for them and listen to what they have to say, but it does take some time usually.

In some cases, survivors may have been abused by someone who is still around to help them deal with their feelings. For example, a survivor of child sexual abuse may have been able to develop good relationships with their therapist and so they may feel safe enough to talk about what happened. However, if the person with C-PTSD has not been in therapy or have not dealt with their feelings in this way, they will usually not be able to open up about what happened because it is too painful. This can cause them enormous distress and make it difficult for them to function in everyday life.

This is a lot of information to absorb and thus I have repeated key concepts for you throughout the book. You have more than basic knowledge and can move forward to deal with your case or that of a loved one.

Lightning Source UK Ltd.
Milton Keynes UK
UKHW020708270223
417728UK00015B/1123